THE HISTOR

MOSTON C

MANCHESTER, A VICTORIAN SUPER-PIT

H. L. HOLLIDAY

Dedication

This book is dedicated to the memory of my father,
Thomas Holliday, who during his working time at Moston Colliery
first introduced me to the wonders under the fields of Moston.
I owe to him my great interest for all things geological,
both above and below the ground.

The Author

Harry Holliday, the son of a third generation coalminer,
has had a life-long interest in the subterranean world. As a boy his father took
him underground at Moston Colliery and these trips made a great impression on his
young mind. Although he didn't choose a career for himself in the pits, the seed had been
sown for his lifetime interest in mining, especially in the area of the Manchester Coalfield.

During his National Service in 1954, he was introduced to the science of speleology,
and so became a caver and potholer, working mainly in Derbyshire and Yorkshire, but
also exploring such caves as the Trou du Glaz in France in the 1950s. He combined these
activities with the exploration of old metal mines, such as at Alderley Edge and
Nenthead, with great enthusiasm for over 40 years. Gradually his interest widened
to mineralogy and geology driven by what he saw below the ground.

When forced by ill health to slow up, he became a volunteer in the
Geology Department of Manchester University Museum, where he is
now an Honorary Curatorial Assistant. Coal and coal mining
still remain of great interest to him.

LANDMARK COLLECTOR'S LIBRARY

THE HISTORY OF
MOSTON COLLIERY,
MANCHESTER, A VICTORIAN SUPER-PIT

H. L. HOLLIDAY

Landmark Publishing

ACKNOWLEDGEMENTS

I wish to thank the following people for all their help and encouragement during the writing of my first book: Fr Brian Seale, who sowed the seed that helped me believe that I just might be able to write a book in remembrance of my father Thomas Holliday; Dr Fred Broadhurst, with his wealth of mining knowledge, and Thomas Allen my friend and contact, who had worked down Moston Pit for many years; David Waghorn, for his help and experience with old maps, and the staff of the Oldham Local Studies Centre who were always willing to come to my aid.

I owe an enormous debt to Dr John Nudds, former Keeper of Geology at Manchester University Museum, not only for his encouragement, but for taking on the job of editing my book, and for his unfailing good humour throughout. Also to Erica my wife, there from the beginning, and who threatened, cajoled and encouraged me to the very last word. Landmark Publishing would like to thank Mr G. Hayes for the use of his photograph of the *Failsworth* Locomotive on page 106.

CONTENTS

1
MEMORIES FROM BOYHOOD

Coal pits have always been part of my life, and in my early memories they seemed to be an extension of our home, like a garage or a shed. I just grew up with them and as a child they were places of interest, rather than places to fear. I can't remember being much afraid on my first trip down. Being accompanied by my own father made my first visit just an interesting new place. Stepping into the cage was no more fearsome than getting onto a bus. A miner's lot is a series of shifts, and seen through a child's eyes, I may have seen dad in the morning or the evening, but never both. However he was always around at the weekends.

After coming down to Moston and studying for his under-manager's certificate, father would have had to work up through all the stages in a pit. Initially just a hewer of coal, later a pit deputy, followed by being an overman, and so on up through the ranks. Securing his certificate would not have been an automatic ticket, for becoming an Under-Manager at this pit meant waiting until the current holder of the position retired or moved away. Occasionally, always on a Saturday morning, he would invite me to accompany him to the pit when he had something special to check on outside of the normal working week, and so with joy I rushed to go along. Down below, equipped with helmet and lamp, I was shown places of great interest in this underground world. Only now do I appreciate the true significance and wonders of what I saw all those years ago as a boy. This pit was a special place, a world of fossils, both plant and animal being well represented. I remember father taking me to see in a niche, not very far from the return airway, a magnificent cluster of ferns that had once lived on the land surface, and now long dead and trapped forever in a layer of black shining coal. These fossil ferns were in the area of the pit called the shaft pillar. They had never been cut, hammered, or harmed in any way by the miners, for in a shaft pillar no coal is cut, except to put a passage or roadway through. At that time, me, a shy boy, asked few questions; I just accepted what I was told and shown. He would have been sick of my questions had he been here today, but that is the way of things. We leave our questions until it's too late.

As we made our way inbye, we seemed to be going downhill and soon arrived at a very steep place indeed. Parked at this spot was a wooden man rider of ancient vintage, totally made from wood, standing ready for our use. This underground steep place was called a slant at Moston. The word inbye is the miners' word meaning to proceed from the shaft bottom further into the mine. The opposite word is outbye, this meaning to make one's way back to the shaft and then out.

There were a number of slants at this pit, and in order that they may be differentiated one from another, each slant was given its own number, for example, slant 17 took one down to Big Seam also known as the Roger Coal. The man riders in this pit were called the "Grip", but I also heard it called the "Jag" as well, Jag meaning a miners' train. I remember thinking that it appeared rather crude and home-made. Seven special trucks made up this miners' train, and I was informed that it carried forty men down the steep brow that was the slant. At the bottom of the slant, this steepness lessened and my father and I climbed out to set off walking again towards the distant coal face, somewhere beneath the area that locally is called Daisy Nook.

After a long walk, and a visit to the coal face, my father told me to stand still while he was away. The air was thick with fine coal dust and all intensity from our electric cap lamps was lost because of this dust. I could hear the noise from the coal cutting just ahead of me, lower down the dip, and a great thick chain lay all along the floor. I suspect the other end went down to a coal cutter. When we became reunited once more, we set off back the way we had come in earlier, outbye, or towards the shaft. I began to get the feeling that this roadway, a main haulage way, seemed much larger and brighter than it had been on our way in. The walls of this fine passage looked to have been whitewashed and the floor and ledges looked to have been dusted with whitish sand, actually stone dust. This stone dust, in the event of a gas explosion, by its very weight, held down the coal dust, and thus prevented any chain reaction along the rest of this level as the pressure wave came along. I am not aware of this pit ever having had a gas explosion, or its story would have been shorter and with a different ending.

Somewhere on our left we came to some air doors, which we passed through. Air doors are always in pairs to minimise any leakage of good air to mix with bad, or the bad air to mix with good. These tough wooden doors are made to be self-closing and are very heavy, and hard to push open. It was explained to me that the downcast shaft feeds good air to all corners of the pit, but eventually it makes its foul exit via the return airway and so into the upcast shaft No. 4, the large fan at its top providing the suction. After passing through a second set of air doors, we stood in the return airway. It had hot and smelly air rushing through it, not a place to linger, I thought, as we pushed our way back through those air doors for the second time. It is hard to visualise today, but 160 years ago, at a similar spot in the old Moston Pit, a boy of 8 or 10 would have sat between these air doors, ready to open them for the passage of any miner or coal truck that came along. They sat completely in the dark, listening to distant sounds, the drip, drip, drip, of water from the roof, the sound of air whistling through the workings, or noises like distant thunder when blasting took place to bring down the coal. These poor boys were given the name "trappers". By 1843 a law had been passed that made it illegal for boys under 10 and all females to work underground.

Back in the main haulage way, which was lit by electricity, we were soon at No. 3 shaft bottom, then speeding up to the surface and daylight. Commands and information about who or what was coming up in the cage, was all done by ringing an electric bell by the onsetter at shaft bottom, and that signal was repeated from another place before the cage could be moved. The steam engine at the surface moved the cage at a tremendous speed; changes in atmospheric pressure can give pain in the eardrums during the ascent or descent and the trick that I was shown was to keep swallowing during this time. I was informed that the cage at this pit moved at 88 feet per second, which is about the equivalent of 60 miles per hour, but a little slower when men were being carried. After my first trip it was possible to stand in the cage, more at ease, and watch the shaft walls become a blur, but after one second there was nothing to see beyond the confines of the cage. I remember being frisked to make sure that I carried no matches or cigarettes when going down in the cage. This was a shock to my innocence, for I did not smoke, but I now know, that this was a vital precaution for the safety of the pit. I deem it a privilege to have had the opportunity to visit some of these places with my father, and to remember them with so much pleasure. In the 1930s and early, 1940s the General Manager was Mr Herbert Richford and the Chief Engineer was Mr Harry Speakman.

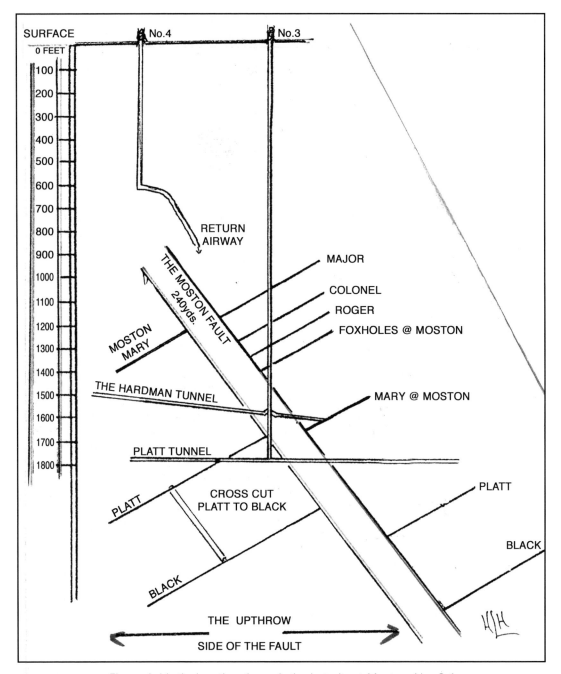

Figure 1: Vertical section through the last pits at Moston, Nos 3-4.

In following Moston Brook downstream from Broadway, in New Moston Manchester the first valley on the right is unnamed; I shall return to this one later. The second valley on the right is called Boar Green Clough. In ancient times if followed to the point where it rose up to the general land surface where the top of the valley levels out, one would come out near to the Copthorn and the earliest pit shaft for Moston; this is the site of the later No. 2 shaft of 1850, and the much later Moston Mill. Much infilling has taken place over the years in this higher end of the valley, with mine spoil from the two shafts, and perhaps rubble from the destruction of the Great Nuthurst Hall after it was pulled down about 1860. As a result, this valley top end became the Millfield with a gently sloping gradient. Rising upwards from Nuthurst Road it has been said that this field once held large heaps of Blue/Gray mine spoil; in my lifetime I never saw any on the Millfield. Nuthurst Road, incidentally, was once called Coal Pit Lane, but at that period was un-metalled even as late as 1915.

At the time when I was a youth, the lower end of this valley formed a major obstacle in the fairway, and by this I mean the Faisworth Golf Course, not the road and houses that came after the golf course had gone. My friend Mike Speakman, son of the pit engineer, and I often looked at the tunnel end that emerged abruptly from the infilled higher valley and we wondered where this water came from, for it was warm enough to send up steam! We ruled out the thought that it came under the golf course from the railway line beyond, for we assumed that signal boxes had no hot water supply. Slowly light began to dawn that maybe our pit was the actual source. Was it the overflow from the pit lodge behind the boiler house? If either of us had asked our fathers we would get swift confirmation, for details like these should have been somewhere on the pit plans; we never asked however. It became our ambition to venture into this tunnel and to follow it to its source, but we were never brave enough to do this. Further down this stream was a man-made, flat, circular area just above stream level. Rumour had it that cockfights took place here, in this circle. Sure enough, a few months later the police raided this place and some men were arrested for playing pitch and toss for money.

The other valley without a name was parallel to Broadway and at one time at its head stood the other old hall, Little Nuthurst Hall. Towards the end of the last war, perhaps in 1946, Manchester had suffered its time of the Blitz, and even though we had won the war, things were still rationed or in short supply. People used to go down to this valley behind and beyond the houses, armed with buckets or baskets to spend a few hours picking small coal from the mine spoil heap that had been tipped down the valley side. At some date after 1935 a temporary road paved with mine spoil had been made across the field from where West Avenue is now. The purpose of this road was to bring that way the mine waste to the valley to be tipped. It is possible that this place became the repository for what started out on the millfield many years before? Though we at home were not short of coal, for my father would have been given concessionary coal from the pit, nevertheless I, and members of our family, came here often to pick a bucketful to serve an aunt or uncle's need. Though the coal picked was small in size, it was bright and shiny and burned well. On one of these gathering days my uncle, who lived nearby, was walking along this temporary road towards the tip and saw what he thought was a coin lying in the coal dust. Stooping to pick it up, he realized that it was a medallion from an earlier time. On one sided it stated, "LANCASHIRE AND CHESHIRE COAL COMPANY RESCUE STATION", and on its back, "Awarded to ROBERT GILL". I have been informed that this medallion is datable to about 1920, a few years before my father came to Manchester seeking work.

Later this tip caught fire and amid complaints from nearby residents because of the smell, water pipes with nozzles were fixed to put out the fire. After more than a year had passed those bad smelling fumes lessened, but it was noticed that some parts of the tip's top surface had subsided. The top surface had sunk in an uneven way due to its smouldering below its surface. When it was certain that the fire had gone out, all of the pipe work was removed and a thick layer of sand provided a new surface. Soon nature took back its own and vegetation grew vigorously again on its top.

Figure 2: The medallion once owned by Robert Gill (Photo H.L.Holliday).

2
EARLY MINING METHODS

The two earliest forms of coal mining were by the following methods. If a coal seam is seen on the surface it is called an outcrop. A long time ago the first man to see and recognize this feature would have excavated an irregular hole in the coal and so would have gathered some. Of what chance event told him that this black coal would burn on a fire just like wood, I have no knowledge. The hole that is excavated to secure some of this rock would usually be to the full height of the seam. If this height was insufficient to allow the man's body to pass, then rock, either above or below the coal, would be prised loose and taken out in order for our "miner" to pass into the hole more easily. The early miner was then free to attack the coal with his tools and thus progress forward. The distance underground that this early miner went was entirely dependent on how far in or away from the light he dare go. However, the addition of a light allowed him to go much further in, but I wonder what circumstances made him first realize that his light could cause a violent explosion caused by gas in the coal. Indeed this first explosion could have been his last. How long dare he mine coal in that unpropped ground, before the weight of the overburden (the rock above) starts to press down into his working space? These mines from outcrop are inevitable found in high country on bare rock and the sides of river valleys. An old word said to describe these early workings is "delf" or "delph".

The second and later form of coal working was called a Bell Pit. This form depended on the operator knowing that the coal was below him at a depth no more than 35 feet. Too deep and he could not carry it up his ladders; too near the surface and the rock roof would not support itself long enough during his coal gathering operation. A simple shaft goes down from the surface with a length of ladder down for access. This was not a commercial operation on a large scale, more a family business with wife and children helping. Hewing of coal by the father assisted by his elder son, while mother and daughters brought the coal up the ladder if the shafts were not deep, or raised it up by a windlass. At the shaft bottom in a bell pit where the coal seam is reached a number of passages radiate out from the shaft. Very importantly the coal between each passage is un-cut, for this supports the roof above, but as a final act the pillars of coal between each passage are robbed out from the outside and inwards towards the shaft. This was the most dangerous time, when large cracks occurred due to pressure, and noises from rock under stress could be heard in the roof. At this stage a wise miner left coal in and came up to start another bell pit perhaps 20 or 30 feet away; the greedy miner may never have come up.

Deep shaft coal mines were still in the future and bell pits were soon to be a thing of the past; debris from their shafts was thrown back in to seal them up. I can't help feeling that there is a great similarity in the layout of the first mines of stone-age man with the bell pits that supplied our coal in the days before deep mines came along. However, both these early methods were inappropriate for Moston, for with almost 200 feet of glacial drift masking any outcrops, no coal could be seen, so no mining was contemplated, and 200 feet is much too deep for a bell pit even if coal was known to be there.

One may wonder on what form of evidence the Old Shaft on the Copthorn (a single shafted pit sunk after 1820) came to be placed just where it was. What facts gave Mr Stanley the confidence to risk a fortune in this, a place where there had never been a pit before? By the year 1820 holes could be drilled, but the hollow drill that could bring up a real core showing rocks and coals in their correct order to be studied on the surface, had not yet arrived. Hollow drills with diamonds around the edges made true cores possible, and it was about 1850 before these first arrived on the scene, so drilling at Moston was not possible at this early date. By the 1840s geologists could not understand why mine owners needed to be so secretive about their mines and why the owners drew no plans of them.

On the other hand, geologists in those early days wanted to get to know their subject better, and to do this they wanted to see geology in the mines beneath the ground where the unknown became visible. At that time the owners kept few plans and any that they had they would not freely show to others. They did not realize at that time how valuable geologists could be to them, but there was no trust between the two factions. It was about 1860 before these two extremes started working together. Mine plans and shaft sections started to be made of many pits and were shared for the very first time, the owners realizing that geology could help them with their problems. Pressure from Parliament came by changing the law so that pit owners had to make maps of their workings. The Secretary to the Manchester Geological

Figure 3: A small diagram of a bell pit.

Society (Mr Mark Stirrup) pleaded with his members, half of whom were owners themselves, to start working together and share the facts with geologists for their mutual benefit.

As far as Moston's first pit is concerned, I expect it was sunk at that time, from confidence gained by seeing the expansion and the success of the coal mines in Oldham, and as the new mines opened, and moved downhill into Chadderton, Moston became a gamble worth taking. The rich men with capital risked it to make more capital, and the good thing that came from this cycle was jobs in the pits for ordinary folk.

Providing the newly sunk pit becomes a success and the coal down below is of good quality, then there are jobs-a plenty for the ordinary man who wants to become a miner. These men, the lowly half of the partnership, took the real risks, for they could lose their lives working in the pit, and until they had a job in the pit had no capital to work on. It wasn't always understood how unhealthy an environment the underground was, with poor airflow and too much dust. The improvement in conditions came very slowly as science strove to understand the mechanics of airflow round the pit, how gas caused explosions and how the so-called safety lamp could fail in one pit, but be perfectly safe in another. Many similar problems remained.

In the early deep mines it was never very safe for a man or boy to travel up or down the shaft sitting on a corve holding on to the winding rope (a corve being a basket used to send up the coal in the days before cages were invented). In an ascent back to the surface the miner, as well as having to hold on, would have to sit on top of the coal, and these corves tended to swing about in the shaft, and sometimes they would hit the shaft sides throwing the miner to his death. A special craftsman who was employed at the pit to make and mend these corves lost his job overnight with the introduction of cages. None of these changes came in isolation; wheeled tubs could not take over from corves until the cage came into use. Cages were just as dangerous in a shaft as corves had been, but the invention of conductors made of wire brought safety to cages, and now trucks could be safely used in the cage. Conductors were fixed down the shaft from top to bottom and acted as a bearing for the cage to run on. Later, tubs were made with metal too for the older wooden tubs were easily damaged in use. Gates for the cages were invented and no more men fell to their deaths below.

The wider pit shafts had a pair of cages fitted now, one at the top unloading coal as the other one filled with tubs at the bottom. Each step forward made pits that little bit safer for the men to work in, and with time the pits got deeper. Moston Colliery was often at the forefront with improvements before new legislation was passed by Parliament. For instance, Moston decided to sink a second shaft for better ventilation (in order to improve the air-flow down the old pit) 22 years before the law was passed making it compulsory for all pits to have two shafts (or one shaft and an adit) as a second way into the mine. Parliament made it compulsory in 1862, but Moston did it in 1840. It is true that by the time of the N.C.B., the colliery was old-fashioned, but after the flood in the old pit, shafts 3 and 4 were given the very best equipment. The new pit ran with the best quality machinery and fittings, making it a State of the Art Pit on opening in 1887.

3
GEOLOGY

Moston Colliery was in the southeast Lancashire Coalfield and geologically belongs to the Oldham Coalfield. Many pits in Oldham mined coal from seams which were deeper down in the Westphalian System than the coals mined at Moston This only goes to show that more upper layers have worn away at Oldham than at Moston Pit; worn away by the effects of wind and rain, frosts and glaciation over the millions of years since the Coal Measures became the surface of the land. A general rule in Lancashire is that the nearer to the mountain chain the coal mine is, the lower in the system the coals will be. In theory the coal-bearing measures in this part of Lancashire could be up to 5,000 feet thick, but only at the late Bradford Colliery in the Central Manchester Coalfield and, perhaps the pits about Ashton and Dukinfield, could anything like this thickness be expected and was never explored or attained.

Moston was lucky in having in its range what in the old days would have been described as the Upper Middle Coal Measures of Westphalian A and B age. These include two of the richest coals in the whole of the coalfield, the Ashton Great Seam (called Colonel at Moston), and the wonderful Roger Seam (called Big Mine at Moston Pit). If Moston Colliery possessed one thing that was record breaking it was that coals were the most steeply inclined in the whole of the county with the exception of some coals at Burnley.

In 1904, in a Presidential Address to the Manchester Geological Society, Mr John Gerrard, H.M. Inspector of Mines, after talking in a general way about conditions in the coalfield, stated that though many pits had steep inclinations to contend with, these conditions did not help in the production of coal or add in any way to the safety in mines. These steep inclines added to the difficulties of setting timbers underground, as well as adding costs for the increase in timber used. He stated that many pits had inclines of 40° or 45°, but the very steepest inclination that he knew of was in the Moston Colliery, which was as high as 51°. This is extremely steep for men to gather coal. He did not specify which part of the mine this record breaking incline was in, or indeed if this steep place affected only one coal, rather than a general effect that influenced all horizons in the mine.

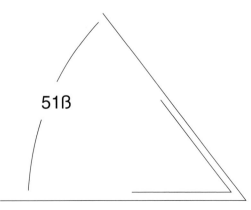

Figure 4: A small diagram illustrating steep angled coal measures at Moston Pit. Angle of dip is 51° degrees.

In 1885 when No. 3 shaft was being sunk, the dip of the measures were being taken and these were the readings in the upper third of the shaft:

at 569 feet down the dip of the measures was 40° degrees,
at 645 feet down   36°
at 693 feet down   35°
at 702 feet down   34°
at 822 feet down   32°
at 882 feet down   34°

In 1931 some official tests were done on coals from various pits in the region and these were published. The following are the results from Moston Pit Coals:

Platt Brothers Holdings
House coals at 600° Fahrenheit

MAJOR SEAM   )
COLONEL   ) Ash 2.8 Volatile Matter 39.9 Calorific Value 14,300
BIG SEAM (ROGER))

Whether these three coals were combined to give an average result, or if each coal was processed separately and the results came out all the same is not known.

The ash content in the above coals was incredibly low; it has been said that at other pits in the area it could be even lower than at Moston, but at Moston the Roger Coal was a thicker and cleaner coal seam, with fewer stone partings to interfere with the quality. Faults play an important part in coalfield geology, if only in the disruption to the seams and their places in the measures. Some of the coals worked at the time of the earlier pits, Nos1 and 2, were still available in the later colliery. The fault itself is no obstacle providing the coal can be found on the other side of each fault. In the new pit, coals had been brought up on the upthrow side of the Moston Fault, from much deeper down and these coals did not exist at all in the old pits up on the Copthorn.

4
Was Lennardine
a coal district at Moston?

In his book entitled, *The Moston Story* (1984), Fr Brian Seale says that James Chetham of Nuthurst, left in the hands of his executors, his will for the payment of his debts, dated 31st January 1613. He desired that all his lands should be divided into three equal parts, one to his wife, one to his son and heir, and the final third towards his four daughters' education. The important part of his will for me is the following:

"James Chetham also owned several messuages & tenements in Crompton, and also the issues and profits, setting and letting, of "one cole myne" commonly called and known by the name of Lenardyne, and with liberty to set down more shafts, and to dig and mine for the finding and getting of coals, shall be and remain to his executors, for and towards the payments of his debts."

In 1984 Fr Seale suggests that the coal pit called Lenardyne could be an early pit situated here at Moston, based upon the will and the fact that James Chetham came to live at Great Nuthurst Hall. This is unlikely for the 190 feet of sands and clays laden with water above the coal seams was an insurmountable obstacle at this early date. The reference to Crompton in the will is the key. I found references to an earlier ancestor, also a James Chetham, who in 1474 leased land in Crompton near to the present day Shaw, to build a textile mill. His home at that time was called Crompton Park. I suggest that the later James moved down from Crompton Park to live at Nuthurst, but his coal mine was at Crompton not Moston. Lenardyne was never here at Great Nuthurst Hall. On the first Geological Map, c. 1865, of Crompton and Thornham, on the roadside across from the top of Narrow Gate Brow stood an old wayside cross, which is no longer visible today, but was marked on the map and was called Leonardin Cross.

Each time I see Lennardyne it is spelt differently. Within half a mile of the cross in various directions are coal workings, and I am quite satisfied that this was the spot mentioned in the will of James Chetham regarding his coal mine. Soon, however, I was forced to the realisation that Lennardyne must refer to a much larger district, rather than just one spot on the map at the roadside cross. I next found a reference dated 1522 when a Richard Wylde was paying rent for the getting of coals at this place called 'Lennardyne', and this place was described as being near to Crompton Fold. Crompton Fold still exists today, but is in an area quite some distance from where the cross of Lennardyne stood. Furthermore, this information goes on to name three coal mines working in the area at this early time, 1522, namely Lennardyne Coal Pit, Low Crompton Coal Pit and Holebottom Coal Pit.

I think this shows clearly that the pit called Lennardyne, mentioned in the will of 1613 was situated at Crompton, this being the newer name for the district; and today part of this area is called Shaw in Lancashire, standing upon a place of ancient vintage.

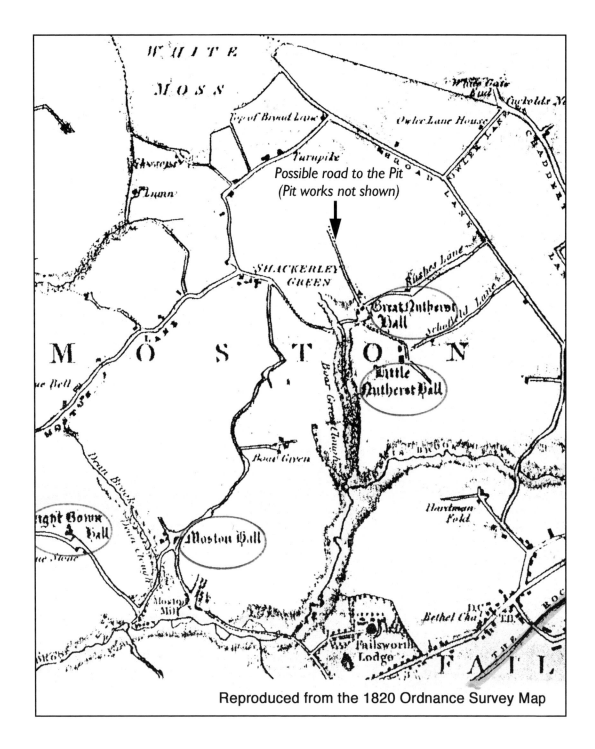

Figure 5: An early map of Moston of old and dated 1820. It shows the Old Halls, Great Nuthurst and Little Nuthurst as well as Moston Hall and Lightbowne Hall. No indications of a coal pit but 28 years later a map shows Old Coal Pit on the site of Moston.

5
THE OLD SHAFT
ON THE COPTHORN

In 1820, industry is sadly lacking as are the signs of ordinary habitations, so perhaps the purpose of the map (Fig. 5) is to show roads and trackways crossing the district, not metalled in the modern sense like we have today, more muddy cart roads and grassy tracks. The Rochdale Canal, seen bottom right, was completed in 1804, being the first canal connecting Lancashire to Yorkshire and taking 39 years to complete. The big houses are prominently marked, for their owners were the true land owners in the district, and no doubt had some say in what went on in their area.

Although this early map of Moston shows no signs of a coal pit or mine shafts, it does give a hint of activity in the form of a short length of roadway running north from Great Nuthurst Hall. It is possible that this road was used to gain access to the first ever shaft sinking at Moston; this shaft came to be called The Old Shaft on the Copthorn. If road it is, this can still be seen on the later map of Moston, dated the 3rd of March 1848, and the pit itself is shown quite clearly marked beyond the end of it. I am sure that the map makers did not leave off an important industrial site like Moston's very first pit, so the answer must be that the shaft had not yet been started. I suspect from this slim evidence that the Old Shaft and Moston's first pit was not completed until after 1820. At this date most coal pits would have operated with only one shaft for each pit.

Today's Geological Maps show quite clearly where each coal seam outcrops on the true rock strata below the overlying drift. However, these details were not known to the sinkers of the very first shaft at Moston, so a borehole in the hope of seeing some traces of coal was all that could be relied upon, if indeed one was ever bored. The sands and gravels are called the "drift", and at Moston Pit they are exceptionally thick, so when the first shaft was successfully sunk, it was described as something of a miracle, but more of this subject later.

Copthorn, a small area of higher land is unknown to Mostonians of today, yet there was once a reference to "The Old Shaft on the Copthorn". Does "old" in that context mean old,very old, or just older than a shaft that came later? I strongly suspect the latter. There is a difficulty with old maps; these features and roads that we know today did not exist 160 years ago. Shafts will be shown isolated in a countryside devoid of houses, and any roadways are just track ways and unsurfaced. Map makers made errors too, by miss-siting shafts on the map or as has already occurred in the Moston district, Clay Pit was misread and then entered on a later map as Coal Pit. Aware of these types of pitfalls, I began to hunt for maps of this area where the pit shafts were sunk and from these I can say the following with some confidence:

- The *Old Shaft* was left off later maps, when the new shafts were sunk. I think that No. 1 shaft was sunk because of the Old Shaft's narrowness and is seen on the 1848 map.
- No. 2 shaft came to replace the Old Shaft. This is seen on the 1863 map and called the New Colliery (210 yards or 630 feet to the Great Mine Coal) and later deepened, to a final depth of 1,008 feet.
- The so-called Ashton Great Mine Coal was always called Colonel Mine at Moston and some other pits. The Roger Seam was also mined from this shaft lying 45 feet below the Colonel Seam.

On the 1848 Map, *Old Coal Pit* is shown as well as the shaft called No. 1 sited near to Nuthurst Bridge. According to records No. 2 shaft would be completed within two years of the publication of this 1848 map. The 1863 map is the last time the Old Shaft on the Copthorn is marked on any map, the wording again being *old coal pit*.

It seems clear that the Old Shaft on the Copthorn, being the first shaft for the pit, was sunk in the 20 years between 1820 and 1840, this latter year being when No. 1 shaft was completed. Some confusion existed over the numbering given for each shaft especially in the minds of ex-miners of the pit. This was first suggested by Seale (1984), and put simply, how can the shaft at Nuthurst Bridge be No. 1 if an older shaft existed at the far side of the Millfield for this same pit? Boreholes are usually drilled to test the measures and find seams of coal, and if coal is not found of a sufficient thickness, this borehole saves the enormous costs incurred in sinking a mine shaft. (It's better to bore to help you explore.) I only found one borehole close to the pit's 5 shafts and this has been given the number 27 in times past. It seems to have been drawn in on the earlier 1863 map and is given the number 4, this number being still used on the 1923 edition.

This borehole stands very close to No. 2 shaft of 1850. A second hole was bored standing in the grounds of a sponge cloth mill at Chain Bar, originally given the number 5, but later called No. 26, this being quite near to the Old Shaft. No. 25 seems to be the number given to a further borehole near to Clough Top actual sited in a cricket-field. Which of these holes were to prove coal for Moston Pit, I really cannot answer, but there is another possibility worth considering. Some may have been bored about 1920 to test the theory of the pre-glacial channel see later chapter).

I suggest that the Old Shaft came first, followed by No. 1 shaft sunk to modernise the pit by introducing the two-shaft principle for improved ventilation. The Old Shaft's narrowness spoiled the efficiency of No. 1 shaft so it was soon decided that a new wider shaft was required to replace the Old Shaft; this new shaft became No. 2.

> The Moston Pit Borehole situated on Little Copthorn Hill
> DRIFT to 189 feet N.C.B. allocated it No. 27
> PyM at 386 feet (This is the Pottery Seam of Lancashire)
> Remainder thin coals and shales down to 456 feet

There are no real clues to the age of the shafts to be found in the style of the headgear above them. The Old Shaft and No. 2 both had pitch pine wooden headframes and No. 1 at Nuthurst Bridge was built with state-of-the-art steel girder headframes. By 1858, John Stanley, the sinker of the first three shafts for the pit, had died. This man of foresight was the driving force who had conjured up a colliery where there had never been one before. In 1858 Moston Colliery was in the hands of his executors. John Stanley, born in Cardiff in 1786, at some stage in his mature life came up to the district of Ashton-Under-Lyne. This man was gifted with the knack of owning successful businesses, and was said to own a mill and at least one iron works as well as some shops, one of these being on Stamford Street in Ashton. From 1840, Moston Colliery was the plum in his empire and his nephew, also a John Stanley, was brought up from Cardiff to become the bookkeeper at Uncle John's pit. Nephew John lived at Shackerley Green just a stone's throw from the Old Shaft on the Copthorn. [Shackerley Green, now forgotten by Mostonians, lay near the present Lightbowne Road.]

In 1858 Platt Brothers of Oldham, in partnership with the Railway Steel and Plant Co. and the Broughton Copper Co., took over control from the executors of the late John Stanley. He did not live long enough to make old bones as the saying goes, but he did see his third shaft brought into operation and his pit becoming a great success in an ever expanding market.

Details of the shafts at Moston

The Old Shaft sunk by	Mr John Stanley after 1820	sited near to Lightbowne Road.
No. 1 shaft sunk by	Mr John Stanley in 1840	sited near to Nuthurst Railway Bridge.
No. 2 Shaft sunk by	Mr John Stanley in 1850	sited near to the later Moston Mill.
No. 3 Shaft sunk by	Platt Bros Holdings in 1887	sited lower down St Mary's Road.
No. 4 shaft sunk by	Platt Bros Holdings in 1887	sited on the same site as No. 3.

The actual sinking through the sands and gravels of the glacial drift, was the really hard part of shaft sinking at Moston. The sands at some depths were called sinking or running sand, and could contain vast quantities of water. At these places the shaft sinkers ran the risk of being buried in sand or drowned by the waters that ran in with the sand. Fifty years after the sinking of the Old Shaft at Moston, Mr. Walter Evans, a mine manager stated the following in 1877:

"There is no doubt that in many districts where the metals are covered with a considerable thickness of quicksand, &c., that sinking through these deposits has been, and will be, avoided as long as possible, owing to the difficulties expected to be encountered when sinking through deposits of this nature is commenced. The time is quickly coming when these difficulties will have to be faced; they are of no trivial character, and cannot receive too much consideration from those who are likely to have such sinkings to contend with".
(Proceedings of the Manchester Geol. Soc., 1877, Vol. 14)

These words, as late in time as 1877, illustrate how big the problem still was of getting through the sands and clays that we call the glacial drift, and show what a triumph John Stanley's very first shaft was when successfully sunk, 50 years before.

At the date of the sinking of the first shaft at Moston, most pits would have had only one shaft of small diameter, just designed to fit a single corve, the corve being a specially made basket in which the coal was brought up to the surface. The miner ascending, had no option but to come up to the surface sitting uncomfortably on the coal, his hand clasping a loop of rope. With time the number and arrangements of these corves was altered as the pits strove to wind more coal quicker. A cluster of three small corves were tried, all three tending to rub on the shaft sides in moving, the only advantage being they were smaller and lighter to be pulled off the hook by the banksman up at the surface. As shafts became wider, two larger corves were tried, one moving upwards as the other descended but always there was banging or scraping on the shaft walls and if one corve touched the other, men could be flung out to their deaths below. The ropes that the corves were attached to, because they were twisted in manufacture, imparted a spin as the corves were lowered in the shaft. This spinning motion made the men riding on the coal dizzy so that they were less able to keep a tight hold on their rope loops. No changes lessened the death rate in mine shafts until corves were replaced with cages with shaft guides. Moston's first shaft was not very successful so thoughts were turning towards other ways of bringing up coal and taking men down to work 1,006 feet below Little Copthorn Hill .

The interchange of air down a one-shaft-pit is always poor. Air was necessary to breath; gas coming out of the coal had to be dispersed by air movements, so air flow had to be improved or induced by mechanical aids starting with bratticing, a form of partition set down the whole depth of the shaft and along each roadway. The dusty atmosphere made good ventilation essential, so at one side of a bratticed shaft a brazier full of burning coals speeded up the rising bad air, the (upcast air). This then sucked more fresh air down the other side of the shaft the (downcast half) and so to the pit bottom. The partitioning of the shaft however, forced the coal owners to use smaller corves so shafts were sunk of larger diameter to compensate for this. Bratticing, started off as a coarse form of cloth, but wood or sheets of metal could also be used as a way of separating clean cold air from the warmer bad air that always moved towards the way out. Weather also played a part in airflow. Cold air down one side of the bratticed shaft circulated round the workings warming up as it did and eventually exited up the same shaft by the other side. Warm days at the surface made the air flow very poor, but cold days up top gave renewed vigour to the natural ventilation. This pit's first shaft was in the early period just before true mechanical ventilation came into use but with the addition of a second shaft things would surely improve, this coming in 1840. Steam power as a motive force had been long in use for pumping out pits. The idea that fans could send air around the pit was soon to come over from the continent to be accepted here as well.

Moston Colliery was said to have always been a wet pit. Had its first shaft not been as deep the water could have been wound up in metal buckets from the sump that is below a shaft. This method was not used but steam powered pumping was utilized, for this method had been long used in the pits of Lancashire to clear the water. Water pumped up to a reservoir at the surface was called the house water, and was utilised in the boilers to make steam. Any surplus water after the reservoir was filled, would have been run away into the small stream in the bottom of Boar Green Clough and so down to the Moston Brook. The later shafts for this colliery received water into new lodges always from this same source, the Old Pit, gravity feeding the new pits ever increasing water needs. A rule of thumb regarding water in a pit would be that the deeper the pit the less trouble it has with water coming into the workings, but there are exceptions to that rule and this pit was one of them.

The Old Shaft on the Copthorn would have been brick lined from top to bottom, for that was how it was done up to the late 1860s in the Manchester area. The bricks would have been handmade locally, and the lime mortar would invariably have been produced from Ardwick Limestone. Ardwick is a district near to the centre of Manchester, and the limestone bands were extracted entirely underground from below a small hill overlooking the River Medlock. From the records of these workings it seems that the lime was superb for shaft lining, slow in setting, but very hard and waterproof when set. The twelve limestone bands were situated in the Upper Coal Measures of Westphalian D age, perhaps up to 400 feet below the surface and mined underground, with no quarry at the surface. Water may have been a problem in the limestone mine as well for in its last phase of working it was used as an underground reservoir for industrial usage. On looking back from a later time, it is easy to think of a pit as primitive, but what is now seen as primitive had once been the last word in technology for that time. The pressure to improve seems to be always on the next generation and improvements come mainly for commercial reasons. The limitations to our first pit are obvious, but the pit got to grips with its problems early by planning for a new, more modern, larger diameter shaft, with the very latest machinery and fittings. The new shaft called No. 1, came in 1840, and was in the very modern style. Corves were done away with, replaced by cages for the men and coal. The cage itself was stabilised by conductors to prevent swinging of the cage in this wider shaft. Down in the sump below the shaft hung heavy cheese weights to keep the conductors tight as a bowstring to ensure a smooth cage run down the shaft.

It is to Mr John Stanley and company's credit, that the two shaft principal was accepted so early at Moston, for it was still 22 years before Parliament brought in an Act in 1862 (25-26 Vict., c79) to force all pits to have two shafts to each pit (or one shaft, plus a sloping level called an adit or day eye). When this was passed its said that half of the pits in the country closed down rather than accept the new law and the expense of a second way down.

Reproduced from the 1848 Ordnance Survey Map

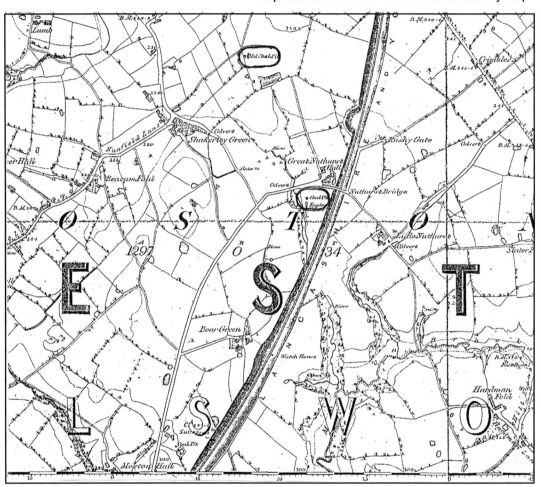

Figure 6: An Ordnance Survey Map of Moston dated 1848 showing the first two shafts (ringed).

In looking back into the history of coal mining, the further back in time, the less we actually know, for little was ever written down. The early pits were started by the landed gentry, very often under their own parks and fields, although they never took coal from under there own houses, for it was soon learned that to do so caused structural damage. The secrets of these one-owner pits was never shared in early times. Our knowledge of where coal was taken from, or even where on today's land surface an old shaft may lurk, is often gone from memory until a shaft suddenly reappears, or a front garden slips quietly into a large hole that was not visible the day before. It is from this scenario that the minute array of facts about Moston's old shaft comes down to us today.

Historically, it is thought the Romans used some coal when they occupied this country and built their forts behind the Roman Wall, for coal residues have been seen and excavated by archaeologists. Saxon sword makers used coal to give the metal some temper, but the amount used may have been small, and their sources for coal could well have been from outcrops rather than coal mines. Until the time of Henry VIII, coal was not popular with the people in their houses because of its smoky smell and its ability to coat the walls with soot. What made coal become more acceptable, was the building of chimneys in new homes, and this only came about in the time of Henry VIII; only then coal could burn without contaminating. It has been said that the earlier pits, supplying the towns and cities in the south of Britain, delivered the coal by sea; coal mines along rivers also had some of those advantages of delivery, hence the early name for coal: sea coal. The canals came next with boats delivering the coal to market more cheaply than before. I suspect that Moston's early pit had access to a coal wharf on the Rochdale canal at Newton Heath at least until 1839 when a new invention, the steam railway, came to Moston. The pits that had no accessibility to water for transport had to sell coal from the pit yard or their local depot; these pits were called landsale collieries, and Moston's first pit had to be one in this latter category.

While the pit had only one shaft, they were increasing production in a limited way, but thinking to the future with a second shaft. The next development rather speeded things up for the pit, and brought a whole new impetus when a railway line into Yorkshire was proposed to pass near by. Nothing could move coal quicker to another place, and nothing needed coal more for its own operation than the recently invented steam locomotive. Plans were drawn up to make the railway work for the pit, but this pit was working for the railway and their mutual benefit. Railway sidings were planned to take coal from the new shaft to be sunk at Nuthurst Bridge, down to join the new railway line.

6
THE SINKING OF
NOS. 1 & 2 SHAFTS

In about 1836 there was talk of a railway line planned to pass close by the pit at Moston. This news speeded up plans for the new shaft for it was soon realized that to take full advantage of the railway for transporting Moston's coal, sidings would have to be built to enable the pit to convey its coal down to join with the new line. By this route the coal that had once been sold mostly locally, could now travel into Manchester, or the other way to Rochdale. The pit was lucky in that it owned or was able to buy at that time extra land which adjoined the railway's planned course. Some of this land ran parallel with the track, and so it was easy to lower the level of the land as the sidings for Moston ran down to meet the coming railway which at this point was in a deep cutting. The cutting was made wider with the addition of the Moston pit sidings. Proof that the coming of the railway influenced the pit's plans is seen by the fact that the new shaft was sited only thirty yards away from the railway and near to Nuthurst railway bridge.

Figure 7: The pit and its surroundings.

The Old Shaft on the Copthorn was situated at a small ridge that had been called Little Copthorn Hill. This hill was a short way north of the place which in later times was the site of Moston Mill, the ridge running east to west. After I had begun this book I sought out a series of maps showing the area of the pit shafts. A surprising thing is that the Old Shaft was never close to the later No. 2 shaft, the Old Shaft being as near as can be determined on the edge of, or even below, the road that we now call Lightbowne Road (first metalled in 1922). Later maps left this Old Shaft off completely. No. 2 shaft, however, was sited about 150 yards further east and so stood in the ground behind the Moston Mill built years later in 1910. No. 1 came first and was the second shaft sunk, sited near to Nuthurst railway bridge (Nuthurst Road before being metalled was called Coal Pit Lane), the bridge and railway along with the No. 1 shaft being planned simultaneously. At the bottom of No. 1 shaft, as well as coal loading facilities, a main haulage way underground was driven to connect with the old shaft at the far side of the Millfield (my name for this area). This connection was an essential part of the two shaft principle for Moston Colliery, and its drive for higher production and better working conditions for the men.

For ventilation, a pit with only one shaft has to rely for its air flow on bratticing, as mentioned before. For this method to be successful, the brattice must be continuous down the shaft and along all roadways to the far end of the pit. A fire bucket, sometimes called a cresset, was hung full of hot coals in the upcast half of the shaft to urge out the bad air and speed up the airflow round the pit. With the addition of a second shaft in the same pit, no bratticing is required because the second shaft creates a new vigour never experienced before. Some pits at this date had furnaces built into the last section of their return airway, but Moston was never one of these. However the air was induced in a pit, just moving it in one direction helped to disperse gas as it was released in cutting coal. Successful mechanically driven ventilation fans were in operation as early as the 1850s, after No. 1 shaft was completed. However by the design of the engine house and the general look of the pit buildings that clustered about the shaft, I suspect that a fan of some kind was eventually used. No. 1 shaft was always listed as the upcast shaft and this strongly suggests mechanical ventilation and the power source being steam.

When two shafts are linked below ground, and a ventilation fan fitted at one of these shafts, this shaft is then known as the upcast shaft for the pit. In drawing out all the heat and the gasses from the passages of the mine, fresh cool air is then drawn down the second shaft. This is then called the downcast shaft for the pit. This two-shaft principle came to Moston only when No. 1 shaft at Nuthurst Bridge was sunk. When two shafts were in use the old shaft on the Copthorn would become the downcast shaft for the pit, and after 1850 its role would be taken over by the newly sunk and completed No. 2 shaft.

No. 1 shaft (upcast) sunk by Mr John Stanley, date of completion 1840
Glacial Drift down to 174 feet. Total depth of shaft 978 feet
Big Seam (the Roger Coal) at 852 feet down, was called first the Stanley Coal
A normal vertical section down to 978 feet
N.C.B. shaft reference No 28 at Nuthurst Bridge

It was the famous George Stevenson, the son of a colliery engineer, who planned and executed the new railway line running from Lancashire into Yorkshire. I can't help wondering if all early railway lines were planned to pass close to successful working pits. It was in both their interests, with one carrying the coal away to the pit's customers, and the other requiring coal to be able to do the job on behalf of the pit. A fact perhaps not well known is that the heyday of the canal system passed within twenty years of the coming of the railways, and steam trains came out on top as the main form of transport for moving coal.

In 1840, the first coal was wound up No. 1 shaft, this being much wider in diameter than the old shaft. A fine state-of-the-art steel headframe was built over the shaft and a splendid modern engine house suggested an up-to-date steam winding engine. At this date the first shafts in Britain were being arranged for cages to wind coal as well as men. If cages are to run smoothly, conductors of wire are fitted down the shaft sides to stop the cages swinging about or banging together if two are in use in the same shaft. This new system allowed wheeled trucks to be used and these ran on iron rails both above and below ground. Overnight corves became redundant. Conductors were an early form of shaft guide, and consisted of wires hung down the shafts for the cages to run on. At shaft bottom, often in the water sump, heavy weights called cheese weights were hung on the wires, to keep the wires taut, and keep the cages apart in their own shaft space. Progress did away with the wire ropes and new forms of shaft guides were tried and improvements made.

If, as suspected, an early form of ventilation fan was fitted at this new shaft (as its name 'upcast' suggests), then this pit had moved into a new league, and became a pit with the latest ventilation technology. The men who worked below would have felt safer, with two shafts rather than just one, both connected below ground with miles of passages between. The job of cutting coal had not ceased beyond the old shaft and the men would joke that they could soon break through into the cellars at the Gardeners' Arms, a local inn; for working to the rise all coal cutting would take place uphill, towards the surface. Under the two shaft principle all coal would now be brought to the surface at the new shaft No. 1 with its modern facilities near the railway. The old shaft beyond the Millfield had lost some of its importance, but a new era had opened for this pit.

When I use the term 'Rise Pit' or working to the rise, this means quite simply to cut coal only in an uphill direction or to mine coal above shaft bottom. In those early days before pumping was mechanised, any water coming down to shaft bottom had to be wound up as was the coal. A rise pit delivered the water at one place. Only with the advent of modern pumping and winding systems could a pit venture below shaft bottom for its coal.

Calculations were made regarding airflow per minute through the passageways of the pit now that it had all the benefits of two shafts. Men could be seen holding strange propeller devices; these new instruments called anemometers measured the speed of airflow at various places below ground. This had not been measured before when there was only one shaft, for the flow of air was so poor. After a few

Figure 8: No. 1 pit, near to Nuthurst Bridge (Photo reproduced with kind permission of Fr Brian Seale).

Figure 9: No. 2 pit headgear still standing erect in 1915, northwest of where the later Moston Mill was built. (Photographed in 1922 and reproduced with kind permission of Fr Brian Seale).

weeks of testing and a few days of debate, it was soon realised that the airflow should have been better. Even though the new shaft's diameter was bigger and the fan was working well, the movement of air down in the pit, though much improved, still left something to be desired. It is a fact that moving air in a rock-cut passage slows down, due to friction from the walls. It was thought that the Old Shaft on the Copthorn was just too narrow, and so worked against the new fan ventilation.

In simple terms the upcast shaft was trying to pump out more air than could easily be replaced down the old narrow shaft on the Copthorn. The solution was there for all to see; a second new shaft would have to be sunk of bigger dimensions to replace the old shaft and it was needed now. It was agreed that this was the way to go, but they had gone through a period of constant paying out, to the shaft sinkers, for new pit buildings at No. 1 shaft, for state-of-the-art machinery and a steam engine to apply the power. Plans were drawn up, but the actual work had to bide its time until the bank balance improved. It was a full ten years before shaft No. 2 was ready to take over from the Old Shaft on the Copthorn. which then could be laid to rest.

At Nuthurst Bridge, No. 1 shaft had been fitted up with the very best that money could buy, but sights were lowered for the coming new shaft called No. 2. Equipment, when ordered, was not quite so good. For instance, it had been decided that a wooden headframe was to be placed above the new shaft when complete; this was the first saving, for pitch pine cost less than the more expensive steel girder headframes that were just coming into use. This set the scene for a saving in costs for the new pit shaft. However, pumping equipment could not be skimped, for Moston Colliery was a wet pit so its pumps had to be efficient and of good quality.

While savings were being made, the centre of operations had moved to No. 1 pit yard. In the days of the old shaft, with one shaft only to bring up the coal, the pit yard and everything else was centred there. Now the hub for all of the pit workings moved to this shaft at Nuthurst Bridge, and stayed there, to await the completion of No. 2 shaft and the expected improvement in ventilation that it would bring. This shaft when completed was in effect just a larger hole for fresh air to go down. Moston Pit had steam power and pumped water up both of its shafts; very soon this modernised pit could mine coal far into the future, or so it was thought.

Sinking No. 2 shaft

No 2 shaft the (downcast) sunk by Mr John Stanley, date of completion 1850
Total Depth of shaft 1,008 feet
Ashton Great Mine at 630 feet, Big Mine (the Roger Coal) at 675 feet down
Normal vertical section down to 1,008 feet
N.C.B. shaft reference No 29

In about 1847, the shaft sinkers came back to the district of Moston, this time to sink the second modern shaft at this pit. All went smoothly, for the measures here were now well understood from sinking the earlier shaft in 1840. Only the upper layers, the 186 feet of glacial drift needed to be watched or mastered as they worked at the shaft, for in these layers much water is stored and the sinkers were not yet in solid stable rock. After the junction was reached with the solid rock, it became only a matter of time before the selected shaft bottom was reached and the connections made with the workings of the old pit and its narrow shaft. As the No 2 shaft became operational, moves would have been made to seal off the Old Shaft on the Copthorn where it met the haulage road.

The Old Shaft could have been left as it was, a further escape shaft, but the management felt that two new shafts filled all the safety requirements that the pit needed. Remember that most other collieries still operated with only one shaft at that date. Another alternative could have been two airtight doors to stop air bleeding out of the system now that they had good ventilation for the very first time. However wooden doors warp and shrink and are soon attacked by fungus, the spores of which are present in all sawn wood. The last thing that this pit wanted was its good air leaking away into an old unused shaft, so this is the reason it had to go.

The answer was to build a dam at shaft bottom and then tip mine spoil (waste rock) into the shaft, or as in earlier times, to put thick wooden beams across the shaft, let into the sides a short way down, and then fill to the top with mine waste. This way, although not so permanent, uses up less spoil in the filling of the shaft. Soil spread over the surface hides the shaft top from public view, and in effect gives the ground back to nature again. Both the Old Shaft and No. 2 shaft were on the grassy area immediately behind where Moston Mill was later built, but the Old Shaft was sited further over near where Lightbowne Road now is. Perhaps a new larger capacity reservoir was built at this time, for pumps were certainly fitted down the new No. 2 Shaft. Boar Green Clough once came up level with the general land surface at a spot on the Millfield. Some mine spoil coming from the early pit shafts would have been used to fill in and level the top end of the clough. The new railway line of 1839 resulted in a wide railway cutting in the middle section of the clough and remember that No. 1 pit had its sidings alongside the railway line too.

Shaft No. 2 was sited where it was, 1,500 feet from shaft No. 1, its position dictated by the position of the old shaft that it was to replace. The layout underground also had a bearing, for ventilation is all important. After 1850, Moston Colliery with its two shafts became a very efficient coal mining unit. The management may have sat back in their directors' chairs, sure in the knowledge that they had done all the right things and taken action when required. They would have felt that they had invested in all of the right things; machinery to ensure the safe running of this pit in the years to come and pumps fitted down both shafts to guard against a flood in the future, From now on a good return was expected from satisfied customers. The last ten years had been a struggle both in developing the pit as well as finding the cash to pay their way. Nothing is certain in this world, however, and fate was to take a hand, 34 years later at which time new owners had come along to take over the pit. By 1858 Mr John Stanley was dead, for documents from the then Inspector of Mines state that Moston Pit was held at that time by the "Exors of John Stanley".

The direction of coal cutting in a pit is rather important; each coal seam that was mined had been followed in a north westerly direction, but cutting at the correct angle to the cleat ensured that the coal came out of the pit in reasonable sized pieces. Larger coals commanded better prices at the point of sale. If cut in the wrong direction, especially in hard coals, a higher percentage of small coals is the result and not many customers required their coal small, least of all the pit itself, for each movement in the pit, like cutting down by holeing or blasting, the shovelling up into trucks, and the washing when done at the surface etc, all tend to lessen the coal's size.

On January 1st, 1874 the ownership of the pit changed. Platt Brothers (the Textile Engineers of Oldham) in partnership with the Railway Steel and Plant Company of Manchester and the Broughton Copper Company acquired the lease of the Moston Colliery. I am unable to say why the latter two companies wanted this pit, unless it was as an investment for profit, but Platt Bros desperately wanted Moston Pit just for its coal alone. Platt's engineering works at Werneth in Oldham was fast becoming the largest producer of textile machinery in the world, and their furnaces would soon be requiring 20,000 tons of coal a year. Platts already had leases on several collieries around Oldham: Butterworth Hall Colliery at Milnrow, Jubilee Pit nearer to Shaw, and the coal workings from Brushes Clough, which had just about hollowed out the hill that stands behind Shaw. Each of these pits were fast running out of coal and about to close down. From Platt's point of view, continuity of supply was all important at this date. Most of Oldham's pits at this time were old pits, working at some distance from their shafts, so with their coal takes nearly finished and each pit closing down, Moston's Coal was the only choice available to meet Platt Brothers' needs.

7

PLATT BROTHERS TAKE OVER

Much of the coking coal that Platts had been using from the lower Coal Measures, and mined off the edge of the Pennine Hills, was once called Ganister coal, but now it is called the Lower Mountain Mine coal. The coals mined at Moston were from something like 2,395 feet higher up in the Coal Measures, but presumably had qualities as a coking coal which matched the needs of the Platt furnaces. However it seems that the coking was not done at Moston.

In July 1874, a company secretary gave his first report to the directors for Moston Colliery. The total assets were given as £21,472 3s 10d. It was decided at the meeting that money would have to be spent immediately to deal with the increasing volume of water which poured down into the workings, this despite both shafts having new pumps in operation. It seemed as if the further northwest the pit pursued the coal, the greater the amount of water that got through to the workings below. A mere two years later, in 1876, more serious flooding occurred, though probably linked to wet weather at the surface.

Platt Bros proposed to install stronger, more powerful pumps, but the other two partners resisted, and during the discussions refused point blank to invest any more money at Moston. Platts were left with no option, but to take over complete control of the pit themselves. On the 1st of January 1877 Moston Colliery belonged to Platt Bros alone. Now with any luck their coal supplies were guaranteed for many years to come, but luck does not come into this equation. The miners had worked steadily on through all these troubles both waterborne, and financial, following the coal ever upwards. The pumps seemed to be coping better, Moston Pit was producing 1,100 tons of top quality coal per week and the assets stood at £96,205 15s 4$\frac{1}{2}$d. It was now predicted that in 5 years time, coal output would have trebled to reach 3,300 tons by 1885, but time was something the pit did not have, for time would soon run out.

In the 60 years of its life, any coals mined had been worked to the rise. In simple terms this means that all coal is obtained upwards from the shaft bottom so in theory, any water troubling the pit makes its way to the shaft bottom by gravity, and is then pumped to the surface from one or both shafts. It was never that simple at Moston Colliery. With its coal lying at a gradient of 1 in 1.5, but in other places at 1 in 2.5, it is inevitable in a rise pit that sooner or later the coals will come to the surface at outcrop. This outcrop would be unseen due to the glacial drift at the land surface. Onward and upward over the years, the miners had chased the coal, and having missed their date with the free drinks in the cellars at the Gardeners Arms, the area of White Moss lay squarely in their sights. They seemed unaware of this as they cut the coals in the direction of the cleat, roughly in a northwest direction.

The six feet thick Roger coal seam had been the chief money spinner for the pit and was an exceptional coal seam, both in quality and cleanliness. Many good Lancashire coals are spoiled by having dirt partings in them, a stony impurity in layers, mixed with the coal. Roger was a fair coal at Denton, a better coal at Hollinwood near Oldham, but at Moston it was as pure and hard as could ever be expected with its one dirt parting down near its base.

One Sunday morning the 9th of November 1884, from some unseen crack or joint in the roof of the Roger seam, a small trickle of water came down into the workings. The hole widened, and in no time at all, torrents of water were cascading from level to lower level, and were slowly drowning the pit. The sound of falling water in the confines of a rock bound passage is an awful thing. It must have given those miners a real shock when they first heard the water coming down towards them, leaping over fallen rocks and accumulating behind air doors and stacked up pit props. By the time the men first saw the waters, it had gathered up smallish pieces of wood from the pit props and with coal dust in its make-up it would have a head on it like a true Guinness from Ireland. Once started, nothing could halt its flow, for water has narrow shoulders and can run through the smallest space.

The men who were cutting coal at the higher workings, momentarily paled, and being only human, fled from it as fast as their legs would take them, given the limitation of their poor lighting in a very dark and now noisy roadway. It was worked out later, that the first rush of water had come into the Roger workings at less than 350 feet below the surface, and that this same coal seam had been worked even nearer to the surface at another place in a different district of the mine. When the fleeing miners reached the bottom of No. 2 shaft, there was such a crush of men waiting for the cage, that many ran on in the hope of reaching safety at No. 1 shaft. They passed down the passage, first in knee deep water and later waist deep, passing the stables that housed the pit ponies. Next came 80 feet of wooden ladder to be climbed, up into the higher 'Colonel Mine' and so on to the shaft at Nuthurst Bridge and safety. Two winding shafts can save more lives than can a single shaft. Those who had ascended by No. 2 shaft were instructed to walk down to No. 1 pit yard for a roll call with the other men, so they all assembled and waited. It was soon realised that all men were safe, and the stress went out of their conversation as they started to relax again, happy to be safe. Medical arrangements would have been made, but were not now required; men from the newspapers had to stay outside on the road which was then called Coal Pit Lane, as they waited for a statement from the management. The ventilation was kept running and the pumps worked flat out in a vain hope that the pit could be saved, for not one person at this time ever thought that the pit would be lost with such good pumps fitted.

Someone at the pit asked if he could go back down, to bring up the ponies, and the under-manager, knowing the difficulties of moving horses in a hurry, asked for volunteers; right away too many men offered. Those that were "putters" with some others were detailed to go, but it was stated that they must not risk their own lives to save the ponies. Putters were the men who led those ponies through the dark roadways of the pit, and the ponies knew their voices, which would have helped more than can be imagined in the watery escape, were it successful. The engine man was given his instructions, and down the men went. Things were not good in the bottom roadway 978 feet below, but the miners were determined and made their way towards the stables. The pit ponies had always been used to some splashing, perhaps some wading as well, but never before had the water come up so far in the roadways of the pit. The putters knew this was not to be an easy task and speed in getting to the stables was of the essence. Blindfolds on the ponies would help them in this task, and they spoke to their charges until all were safe up top.

The ponies would have come up two at a time with the cage. Whether the cage was big enough for two ponies to pass into, or if they had to be hung in a special hammock or sling that was hung from the cage bottom. Suffice it to say that all the ponies came up unhurt, and there had been no casualties of any kind. With joy in their hearts the putters would have led their charges through the pit yard and so to the ponies' field situated at the side of St Mary's Road. While all this activity was taking place a message was sent to Messrs Mather and Platt in Newton Heath pleading for help in the pumping out of the shafts. This firm made pumping equipment and still did during my earlier years. The following day all the miners turned up at the pit yard for work, but it was not sure if there was any work to go to. A party of leaders travelled slowly down at No. 1 pit; the cage had never gone down so slowly before. It was hoped that the waters had receded for pumping had continued throughout the night. But before the pit bottom was reached it became obvious that the shaft landing was drowned and the waters were rising up the shaft itself; nought could be done so the cage returned to the daylight. A similar party had descended in shaft No. 2 and quickly returned for the waters there were too deep to make a landing. Later the new pumps arrived and were fitted in the shaft at No. 2. These were 32 inch bucket pumps with a ten foot stroke, and these two alone were said to be capable of pumping 4 million gallons per day. The pumping was continued for two months, but the waters still rose up in the shafts. Four hundred men and boys had been put out of work and their families were soon starving. By the 12th December the waters had risen up above the point where it had first entered the mine below White Moss and Great Copthorn Hill. A decision was made by the Board of Platt Bros., that the colliery be abandoned, but that new shafts, Nos 3 and 4, would be sunk to the south of No. 1 shaft of the flooded pit.

Escape from the Flood

1   I once stood by a hole in the ground,
And marvelled as to how it was found,
I watched some miners go down that hole,
Down, down, till they came to its sole.

2   They chatted along as they plummeted down,
As the daylight receded above.
They laboured away for all of that day,
Then up to pitbank and their loves.

3   The round I describe was to keep them alive,
As they drove their tunnels inbye.
They all knew one day,they might have to pay,
If Gabriel's horn blew below ground.

4   By following Roger up under White Moss,
The best coal in Lancashire cut for their boss,
But one hole too many, the coals undercut?
A trickle of water and then a great rush.

5   Ponies were left down, the miners all ran,
Most went to one shaft the others climbed on.
They stood in the pit yard, thanking their God,
Near sixty men out, not quite dry shod.

6   So back in the shaft, down to pit eye,
When asked, the putters were glad to say "aye",
We'll bring up our ponies, the least we can do,
To rescue our ponies so they can live too.

7   The ponies came up in the cage side by side,
Unused to the light, they wanted to hide,
They rolled in the pit field, the sky was so blue,
The ponies didn't realise, they were out of work too.

8   The old pit is finished, long live the new,
The shaft sinkers sinking, three's nearly through.
The miners are happy, they're in work again,
No waiting for handouts, forgotten the pain.

9   Platts to the rescue they sank number three,
Sinkers on shift work, blasting night and day,
The old pit's abandoned, the new on its way,
In 1887 they would all work for pay.

H L HOLLIDAY 1996

8
THE CONSEQUENCES OF THE FLOOD

Most of the miners who had worked in the pit were instantly put out of work, with only a small number kept on in order to prepare the new site for the shaft sinkers. The newly unemployed men received no wages for there was nothing in those dark days except charity and a few acts of great kindness. The days of Social Security and the Welfare State were still a long way off in 1884. In the homes of the men who had lost their jobs at the pit, hardship and hunger were now ever present. They had never known luxuries, but they always had food on the table; now they would not have known where the next meal was coming from. The only thing the miners could be thankful for regarding this disaster was that there were no fatalities. However, as always in times of real need, caring people stepped forward to provide for the needy.

Platts donated an amount of money to each miner and a distress fund was started in the area of northeastern Manchester. A philanthropic steeplejack from the district of Oldham by the name of Joseph Bell, brought a cart-load of hammers, picks and shovels to be distributed to the men. The miners had unfortunately abandoned their tools below in their mad dash to escape from drowning. A miner without tools could not expect to get work at another pit; they were his badge of office, a true sign to a potential employer of the miner's competence to work below ground.

Mr Holgate, who lived in St Mary's Road, supplied the unemployed miners with soup, bread and potatoes. Fifty men were given work by Mr James Radcliffe, a manager at the Astley Deep Pit at Dukinfield, but the other 350 men struggled on, waiting for the opening of the new Moston Colliery. Many other acts of kindness took place at this time, but history does not record them. I realize what a mixed reaction the men and their families would have felt when a potential job came up at Dukinfield. First would come elation at being given work at a new pit, bringing the chance of a regular wage after so many weeks of struggle and suffering. Then would come the realization of the logistics involved in travelling to a different town to work, and the woman of the house would inevitably have thought, "when will he come home" or "when will the children see their dad again". It is not easy to know from our vantage point how a miner would have travelled to Dukinfield.

Today we have buses, trains and trams, but the miner would have to walk via the area called Daisy Nook; he would not have had the fare even if there had been buses at that time. He obviously would not have done this journey daily. Did he take lodgings and only go home at weekends? Was his first week's rent on the slate till he drew his first wage? Did they trust him until he was paid? In time all that would have been resolved and the family would no longer be on the breadline.

The Proceedings of the Manchester Geological Society record the flooding of the pit. At an ordinary meeting of the Society, on 2nd December 1884 a paper was read by Mr C.E.de Rance entitled, *The occurrence of brine in the Coal Measures* (de Rance 1884). He states:

"the recently reported case of large volumes of water of good quality being met with in the Moston Colliery near this city, is a case in point, if such waters should prove to be derived from the Coal Measures, showing the quantity and quality of water often yielded by these measures, and which though somewhat uncommon in the Lancashire Coalfield, are so well known in that of Yorkshire".

By the time that this paper was read, Moston Colliery had been entirely engulfed by the floodwaters and although the battle to save the pit still went on, and was at a very crucial stage, with hindsight it can be seen that the battle was already lost. Both shafts were soon to be abandoned and new ones sunk in their places. Mr de Rance's paper assumes that the flood at Moston was coming into the pit from the Coal Measures, but we now know that the waters originated from a near to the surface source (see below).

After the above paper was read out to the members, Mr. Joseph Dickinson, Vice President in the Chair, said that:

"At that late period of the meeting there was not time to discuss the subject fully, but that as the bursting of water into the Moston Colliery was touched upon in the paper and had a local interest, he might mention that in his own mind there was no doubt the water came in from the overlying sand and not from the strata as left by the paper an open question (Dickinson 1884). He pointed out that when about 40 or 50 years ago the late Mr. Stanley succeeded in sinking his first shaft through the sand and soils at Moston, it was considered a great achievement, so many previous attempts having failed. Dickinson explained that there was a covering of sand 60yards or more in thickness, much of which is broken up and mixed with some clay, but at one place a fault in the coal workings may be seen rising through bedded sand (apparently Permian) to the surface of the ground. The fact of this sand containing a large quantity of water had been known for a long time, and he had cautioned Mr. Stanley against working far on the rise lest the water might beak into the workings, and this caution he communicated to the present owners [Platts] on their taking the colliery. He concluded that it seemed that it was about 120 yards [360 feet] below the surface where the water has broken in through the roof of the mine."

Fourteen years after the flooding at Moston this subject was brought up again at a Manchester Geological Society meeting. Mr. Dickinson, after the reading of his paper called *Subsidence caused by colliery workings*, stated:

"in 1884, at the then Moston Colliery, near Manchester, at a part where the workings were 120 yards, 360 feet, below the surface, water broke in from the very thick overlying sand, filling entirely the workings in several seams, which still remain inundated, the present colliery being separated by a large fault" (Dickinson 1898).

Five years later, after the reading of a paper called by Mr. Pickstone, Mr. Dickinson once more referred to the case of the Moston Old Colliery now inundated. He said there was an almost inexhaustible supply, and when the inundation took place the question was gone into as to whether the water should be used for domestic purposes or not, but the analysis showed it was not suitable (Dickinson 1903).

Mr. Joseph Dickenson was a much respected man; he became a member of the infant Manchester Geological Society in July 1856 and remained a key member for 56 years. Born at Newcastle in 1818, he learned his trade in the coal industry and moved about to various parts of the country until he became one of the first four Inspectors of Mines. After being given Lancashire as his main area, as inspector he made his home at Salford and lived his whole life there. He became

M.G.S. President three times, in 1861/3, 1877/8 and 1887/8. He was appointed Inspector of Mines in November 1850 and did that job with great thoroughness for 42 years, retiring from the job at the age of 74 years. His area of duty in the early days was Lancashire, Cheshire, North Wales, Staffordshire, Shropshire and Worcestershire. He was sent into Europe to look at ventilation fans in operation at coal pits there, and advised Parliament on aspects of safety. At a late stage his area as Mines Inspector was reduced to North and East Lancashire where he watched over 240 working coal pits. Whether this reduction was due to his age and the amount of travelling that he had to do, or because many more inspectors had been appointed by this time, I am not sure, but he was a very special man.

Still on the subject of the flood in 1884, I was able to discover the names of the two unlucky mine managers for the pit during those years of trouble. For some years before the flood, the manager was Mr. Charles Cooke who moved on to be manager at a pit near the town of Ilkeston, Derbyshire, in 1883. The new man for Moston was Mr. Thomas Greensmith who would hardly have learned his way about by the time the waters broke in. My sympathies go out to him for he stuck at his task moulding a new pit under the flooded ruins of the old one, and stayed at Moston for many years, seeing the later pit become a great success.

A Very Important Document

During the early years of my research for this book, I came across a copy of a Geological Survey Map, labelled *Moston and Blackley*, undated, but I suspect a 1932 Revised Edition (see Figure 60). It was a lucky find for me because marked upon the map are very pertinent details appertaining to four of the five deep shafts of the Moston Colliery and also a suggestion that there had been an earlier shaft with a borehole marked close to No. 2 shaft.

Areas of land are marked on the map for the surrounding pits: Alkrington Old and New Collieries, Bower Colliery, as well as the area where coal was taken in Moston's earlier shafts. This map shows the area of inundation of 1884, when the pit became flooded and became an abandoned mine. Incidentally, at that time in 1884 the Alkrington New Pit was already flooded and shut down, so the earliest theory regarding Moston's troubles was the flooding of one pit by another. The details from 1884, drawn in on a 1932 map, suggest that a person with knowledge of the pit's earlier history had added these details. It seems quite likely that this person worked at the pit for some time and if so may have been known to my father. The other possibility is that this map came from Platt Bros Holdings, the parent company who owned the pit The name of this person and the circumstances of his knowledge will forever remain a mystery.

In coal mining districts there is a minimum distance of coal that has to be left uncut between any two pits. This safeguards one pit from another, especially if they both mine the same coal seams. Note on this map the probable line of the pre-glacial channel, the now accepted reason for Mostons' flooding. In effect, this line is the earlier course of the River Irk, its valley now infilled with sands and clays from the melting of the ice sheets after the glacial epoch. A circle at the bottom right-hand side of the map had me mystified for some time until I realised that it marked the line of the shaft pillar for the No. 1 shaft that was situated near to Nuthurst Railway Bridge. Coal was never cut out in a shaft pillar, so this became the only safe place to sink new shafts safely through the old flooded workings, the uncut coal acting like a cork to hold back the waters from falling into the deeper pit. This new pit started producing in 1887, but coal was sought in a new direction beyond the Moston Fault and away from the flooded workings 800 feet above. The last two items of note on this map are as follows; two exploratory roadways were driven in the late 1890s seeking coal beyond the fault. Called the Platt and Hardman Tunnels, these can be seen on the map heading a little west of south. Lastly, written in pencil is the legend, 'point of inundation 1884 shown by +', this referring to the exact spot on the map where the flood waters first entered into the roadways and workings of the Old Pit in 1884. (The original map is in the keeping of the Oldham Local Studies Centre.)

9
THE HISTORY OF
THE PRE-GLACIAL CHANNEL

After the flooding of the earlier pit it was always supposed that the flood waters had made their way into the Moston Colliery workings from the already drowned pit at Alkrington near to Middleton in Lancashire. The law states that a certain width of coal is always left in between two mines as a buffer, to save one pit from the other in case of flooding. But of course both pits in this case were flooded, the unknown factor could have been faults in the coal that had been left between the two pits, the fault acting as a channel for the water to flow along.

There was always a danger as well in the quality of the survey work done below ground, for the accuracy of the surveying cannot be checked by the surveyor's eye as can be done at the surface, e.g. the pit headframe to Failsworth church spire, or No. 1 shaft to the tower on Marlborough Mill. From this, one can see that accuracy below ground is all important for the plans can only be drawn correctly if the figures calculated below ground are totally accurate.

In truth the area of coal being taken in the year 1880 at Moston Colliery was rapidly approaching the other pit at Alkrington, but the depth of the coal at the extremity of Moston's workings was less than 400 feet below the land surface. The nearest Alkrington pit workings to Moston's were at a depth of something like 1,271 feet down, so flooding from one to the other, with hindsight, seems rather unlikely.

In 1918 Miss M.C.March was doing a study of the bore holes through the drift. She was not interested in the solid rock below ground, but only in the debris that lay between the soil and the rock. The way she looked at this gave her some idea of the humps and hollows that exist unseen below the glacial drift. The overall picture can show pre-glacial river valleys, for the rivers were often forced to change course and carve out a new valley, often with little similarity to where the river had run before. We now see the present valleys complete with the rivers, but the original valleys are obscured by glacial deposits. As far as Moston Pit is concerned, she thought that she could detect a sub-drift hollow, or possibly the pre-glacial channel for the ancient River Irk (March 1918). I guess that the men of the British Geological Survey (Tonks *et al.* 1931), accepted her findings as a more realistic theory for the flooding at Moston than the earlier one concerning the Alkrington New Pit. The Moston Pit miners, in working to the rise, had apparently broken through into this channel which was not only full of sand and gravels, but full of water as well, right back up to its headwaters east of Royton.

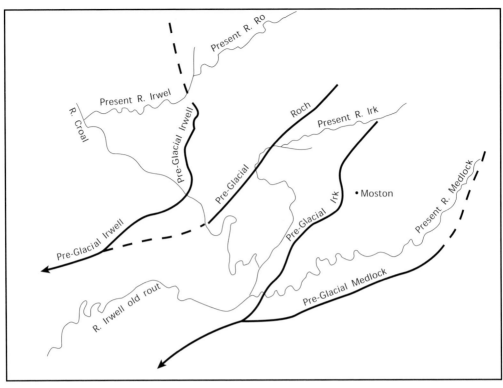

Figure 10: Plan of the present rivers and their possible pre-glacial courses.

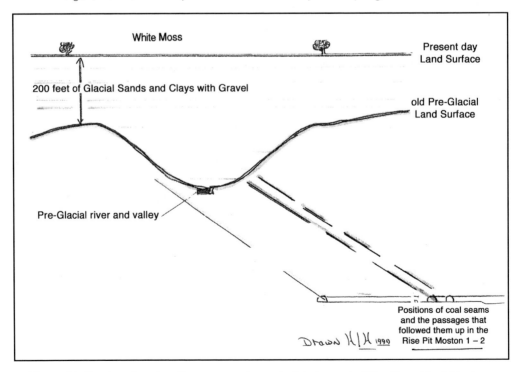

Figure 11: Section showing the supposed pre-glacial channel of the River Irk at Moston.

Worries in Platts' Boardroom

There was another set of worries just up the hill in Werneth, namely in the Platt Bros boardroom, but here they were of a different kind, nothing to do with hunger and losing one's home. Once the decision had been made that the old pit at Moston was abandoned, the thoughts at Platts turned to the planning of Nos 3 and 4 shafts and the new pit. Any wrong decisions taken now could bankrupt Platts and put out of work the 8,000 employees in the many factories belonging to Platt Bros in and around Oldham. They had owned many small coal mines in the foothills of the Pennines between Milnrow and Oldham, but these were now mostly closed down. To avoid a shortage of coal or coke to fire the furnaces, Platts had bought Moston Colliery. It had answered all of their needs in this department, but it had never been foreseen that the pit would be flooded and have to close down. Now coal would have to be bought in for the very first time from other pits, which had, in a way, been Moston Pit and Platts rivals in the coal trade. Out of the first few meetings came a determination to battle on and to succeed with their plans for the new pit. In brief, this was the plan of action.

Two new shafts would be sunk down to the coal, a little west of south from the position of No. 1 shaft. These new shafts would have to be deeper, for the coal seams dipped in a southerly direction, and so were deeper down where the new shafts were planned. Deeper shafts had a further advantage: they kept the workings at a safer distance below the waters that stood in the old pit. It would never have been said, but in effect the new pit would work the ground below those old flooded workings. Time was not wasted. Heenan and Froud were engaged to supply the new steel girder headframe to stand over No. 3 shaft, and a well-built engine house as well. Mr A.E. Wolstencroft, from Platt's Hartford Works, was given the task of constructing the engine house for No. 4 shaft. The engine from No. 2 pit was moved to power the cage in No. 4. The new timber headframe for this shaft was fashioned out of best pitch pine and was made in the Colliery workshop; it stood for 63 years, its last years surrounded in a concrete shell.

The steam winding engine for No. 3 shaft was ordered new, but its maker is unknown. Sinking new shafts was no miners' picnic. The pit engineer, a very busy man at this stage, would have been consulted over machinery and fittings, but many questions could not be resolved early for there still remained many unknowns. Ventilation equipment was now much more efficient than the last time it was required, for No. 1 shaft, so now choices were made in the boardroom. Likewise pumps needed to be ordered. In the first place there were to be pump rods down the whole depth of No. 3 shaft, but later on in the planning stage, it was decided to use electricity to power the pumps.

The power of the engine for No. 3 shaft could not be determined at an early stage for this depended on the depth that the shaft reached, and because of a geological fault yet to be cut through, the depth of the shaft would alter from any original plan. Each move had to be made step-by-step at its appropriate time, all could not be planned initially for there were many questions and many unknowns still to be resolved.

The Board of Directors had to find the money for an indeterminate length of time until the new pit was producing, but in the meantime plans were made and work started in setting out the new pit top, i.e. the buildings surrounding the shafts. A new reservoir was sited behind where the boiler house was going to be built, for boilers and steam must have a great deal of clean water and the water was going to come down from No. 2 shaft to keep the reservoir filled up. The new pit was modern in conception for that date, and nothing was spared to keep it good. Nothing cheap was used at this time and whatever was recommended for the new pit, was sanctioned by the Directors, for Moston's coal was badly needed for the forges and furnaces at Platt Bros factories and workshops in and about Oldham. The planning had been formulated, as much as could be pre-planned, the shaft-sinkers had started work, and this was an area of work that could not be rushed and was to take a full three years in the making. Now all that was wanted was some good luck, but Platt's luck was not good as shall be seen later. However, with perseverance and dedication all was turned to the company's advantage, including their bad luck. Sinking shafts at Moston had never proved easy, but they would be done well, come what may.

Figure 12: Platts sign was fixed to their machinery as an advertisement, 'done with pride'.

10
A LITTLE ABOUT MINE SHAFTS

The job of shaft sinking has always been rather specialised and would have been undertaken by teams of specialists used to working in these most difficult conditions. Working in a deep shaft bottom has to be a most alien place judged by any yardstick. The methods now described obviously altered as time progressed, and new ways were found and tried to make the job safer or quicker to accomplish, but my real concern deals with the methods that may have been used in sinking the various Moston Pit shafts, say from 1800 to 1900.

The shaft sinkers were a breed apart; they had to be strong in the arm and also very brave as they constantly suffered bad air due to rock dust, made many times worse when blasting was used. They would be breathing in harmful fumes from dangerous gases after blasting had taken place, for poisonous fumes could linger at the bottom of a shaft, simply because there was only one way into it, the bottom still being solid rock and no way through. There was no through draft to clear the fumes and bring down new air for the men to breath. Blasting in a confined, area is much worse because the sound is totally confined; the men

Figure 13: A team of shaft sinkers posing at a Cumberland Pit in 1912. Note their wide brimmed hats to protect their eyes (Photo reproduced with kind permission of Anne and Bill Thomas).

were only brought up a short way for the explosion and then lowered back to clear the rubble amidst gases and fumes.

A 'kibble', a large strongly made bucket, was always called a 'hoppet' in the Lancashire Coalfield. In the very early days when shafts were not so deep, the men would have drilled at the bottom of the shaft standing on the rock. A kibble would be swinging to one side ready for their ascent if they were blasting or ready to take rock waste up to the surface. This same kibble was also used for winding water out of a wet shaft. With time and progress came drilling platforms for the men to work from, but a single platform did not give them safety from falling rocks coming out of the shaft side. Later, this drilling platform had a second one located above the men's heads which gave them safety from falling rocks, and the kibble or bucket came down to them through a self-opening trap door set in those platforms. The earlier shafts had to be bricked up from bottom to top to keep any loose rock secure, and also to lessen and keep back the water that ceaselessly dripped in through the shaft sides. Water was the one problem that could stop work in the shaft bottom; generally speaking water problems were much worse near to the surface, and the deeper one went the less water came into the shaft. The sinkers wore special clothes and extra wide brimmed hats to protect their eyes from falling water. For the feet, clogs would be worn, with no such luxuries as wellingtons or pit helmets in those days. When the kibble was taken up to surface full of water, it had to be emptied well away from the shaft, to avoid having to wind up the same water, a second time.

Early shafts were sunk by hand with picks, shovels and wooden wedges; when blasting became possible long chisels and heavy hammers came into use. Much later a whole floor-full of holes could be drilled automatically by the use of many drills that were fixed in a rig using compressed air for power. This set pattern of holes was charged, the first blast in the centre to form the initial hole. This was called the *sumping shot* and it created the hole for the second sequence of charges to move the rocks into from the outer circle of the shaft. All shaft debris had to go to the surface for there is no space below until coal is being cut and the passage layout finished down below. A bore hole could be put down either from the surface, or later from the bottom of an already deep shaft to test the deeper layers for coal, but in early times no drill cores could be brought up, for this kind of drilling had not yet been invented. Coal dust, or slight signs of it, could be detected attached to the clays, but there was no way of accurately knowing how thick a coal seam was by this method. The early pit master-come-geologist had to seek for signs in the mud and slimes that came up on his drill bit. Small-bore hand drills had been used after 1708 in areas away from any outcrops, but depth was limited by friction to about 100 feet and no core came up from this system either. It is said that two operatives using this early drill used percussion to pound up the rock below, and a rotational turning movement to keep the drill free in its hole.

An ancestor of mine in 1825 used this very same hand drilling system to bore for coal in Cumberland. A 2ft 3ins coal was located and a pit sunk 18 fathoms (108 feet) to mine it; from this I can believe that hand drilling worked even through hard rock. A new system that allowed cores to be withdrawn from the borehole was invented in 1804; this allowed the thickness of the coal to be measured and its quality assessed without going to the trouble and expense of sinking a shaft. In sinking a shaft down towards the coal seam, it was always the upper layers that gave the most trouble. These were the layers that were composed of what we call the glacial drift, and were notorious for holding much water in their makeup. In Lancashire the drift can be as much as 200 feet before solid rock is reached, and Moston Colliery was somewhere near this thickness. On old shaft sections the appearance of the word 'quicksand' or 'running sand', suggests a special form of trouble for the shaft sinkers. It is composed of a fine sand, its grains unbound by any clay, and the first sight a sinker would get of this, is when it poured into the confined space that was his shaft bottom and the sand ran in like water. The addition of water to sand takes away the property that makes sand a semi solid, and the sand flows just like it had become a liquid and settles into the shaft with up to about 10 feet of clear water always on top of the sand.

In the sinking of Royton Park Colliery near Oldham, time after time this liquid sand and water came welling up into the shaft bottom, and on one occasion rose up to a height of 60 feet, comprising 50 feet of sand and 10 feet of water on the top. In order to get down to their previous shaft bottom they had to dig out the 50 feet of sand, but to do this the 10 feet of water had to be wound up first, and each time water was taken, more sand and water came in at the bottom

In reading this account I couldn't help thinking about the team of men in the shaft bottom when this sinking sand came in and carried them, presumably safely, 60 feet up in the shaft. But the sinkers were not even mentioned in the whole text; life must have been cheap then. This eleven foot wide shaft was eventually taken down to its planned depth of 756 feet, but the water won in the end, for 27 years later the pit drowned with its pumps overloaded. It had taken 2 years to sink the shaft 176 feet to the first coal, so this left 580 feet in hard rock still to go, but the hard rock was far easier and caused much less trouble.

Another way to get safely through the wet upper layers was called the Caisson Method. This started with the forming of a cutting shoe, a fraction bigger than the required shaft diameter. It was made of iron or steel with a sharp pointed bottom outer edge and circular like a sewer pipe. The shovelling is done from in its centre and the dug out spoil is sent up and out in a kibble or hoppet that is lowered down the inside of the ring from the surface. Meanwhile a team of bricklayers lay bricks on the top edge of the caisson making the circle of the shaft, and if all goes to plan, with the added weight of the brick circles and the digging out from inside of the sands and clays, the caisson moves slowly down into the drift in unison with the work being done. If luck is on your side the hard rock layers below are safely reached. A large problem in this method of shaft sinking is that if the whole column gets out of vertical, it is then impossible to pull it back to vertical. A well-reinforced concrete shoe was another form, but this was only a success for a small diameter shaft. A machine driven "Clam Shell Dredger" could be used with a caisson, and the softer bottom dirt was stirred up and loosened first with a large bladed auger. I have witnessed a small diameter mineshaft being re-opened by this method.

The progress I have just outlined covers the time span of the earlier shafts sunk at Moston. The measures sunk through did contain some thin bands of sinking sand, or quicksand in the upper 200 feet, but these were nothing like those mentioned earlier with regard to Royton Park Colliery. Nevertheless Moston Pit's "Quicksand" did merit a mention in a Welsh book on mining. In 1887 when Nos 3 and 4 shafts were being sunk, no prior drilling would be required, for the measures here were fully understood from the experience gained from the previous three shafts, and the essence for Platt Bros Holdings and the Moston coal was speed. In actual fact the known measures had only been explored at Moston's earlier pit to a depth of 1,000 feet, but great confidence existed in the Platt Bros boardroom that a new colliery, a better safer colliery, could be secured below the flooded workings that was the former pit. When No. 3 shaft was being sunk, three bands of quicksand were sunk through in the first 95 feet of sinking, and the total thickness was just four feet one inch. This may not seem much of a problem, but the sand, when in the presence of water, can deliver many tons into the shaft bottom in a matter of seconds. It seems that whatever we call the sand that was encountered below in shaft sinking, this was undoubtedly met with in the glacial sands and clays near to the surface. However, I was told of a place in the workings at Moston Pit, where dry sand over a long period of time persisted in running down a slope to partially block the roadway. This was sand from a layer that was sandwiched between two hard sandstones not far from the top of Slant 17. It was eventually blocked off with corrugated iron sheets.

Sinking Nos. 3 and 4 shafts (the new pit) after 1884

Water is usually encountered in the upper layers where it is dispersed throughout, but in the solid rocks below the drift water can also be met with, though this is then separated by distance, one spring from another, with layers of rock or coal between. These seem to be more like the springs that one sees in limestone country, issuing out from below a cliff. Below are the depths where water entered the No. 3 shaft as it was being sunk through the upper rock layers, but well below the drift materials:

235 feet down
245 feet down
271 feet down
278 feet down
287 feet down
304 feet down
435 feet down
453 feet down

It was not on the plans how many gallons per minute came in at these points in the shaft, but many details were given, such as the crossing through the shaft of a small fault at 520 feet down. This caused no trouble to the sinkers for it had passed completely through the shaft in 14 feet of depth. Unfortunately this ease of passage was not to be repeated at another much greater fault lower down in the strata (see later). In 1884 Platts spared no expense to make Moston a wonderful working pit again, and this is another sign of that policy. The Ardwick Limestone mine had closed down and no longer supplied the pits of the Lancashire Coalfield with its slow setting cement that had been good for bricking up newly sunk shafts. The new invention that Platts decided to use for their two shafts, Nos 3 and 4, was called tubbing. This system was a great leap forward for coal mines, for as time went on pit shafts became bigger in diameter and tubbing suited bigger shafts for it was fitted as segments of a circle. Years ago pit shafts could be square or rectangular, oval or circular, but by this date (1884) most were being sunk in the circular form. The name tubbing suggests the sides of a barrel, so this may be the source of the name (making the shaft like a barrel). Tubbing was generally cast out of metal or made from reinforced concrete; both types required their joints to be sealed prior to bolting together and in the first years of this system, lead sheeting was used. After bolting together it was recommended that any spaces left behind the tubbing must be filled in with cement, so as not to leave space for water to collect in. Each time a strong band of rock was reached, this was utilised to fit "wedge curbs". These secured the weight of the tubbing down to the next solid rock band, so sharing out the weight of the tubbing as the shaft is sunk further. (See Figure 15 for detailed plan of the wedge curbs fitted at Moston, and Figure 16 for two forms of tubbing fitted at Moston No. 3 shaft.)

The hole that the wedge curb fits into, in a strong band of rock, was never blasted out; it had to be carefully chiselled out by man so that the wedge curb fits very snugly in the hole. If it had been blasted, the rock would have cracked and the strength and the holding power in the good rock band would be wasted. A special ring was built into the tubbing which had a shoulder jutting out on its outside which was fitted into the hole that had been cut out by hand. This arrangement took the great weight of the tubbing and shared it out at various places where the rock was strong. Another method used in No. 3 shaft to spread the weight was an arrangement of 16 girders fixed to the tubbing and keyed tightly into the rock (Figure 18). These were fitted at 570 feet down and formed a super eight-cornered wedge curb made from 18 inch deep x 6 inch broad girders. In 1896 a new short length of tubbing had to be replaced in No. 3 shaft at about the junction of the drift where it rests on the solid. It is

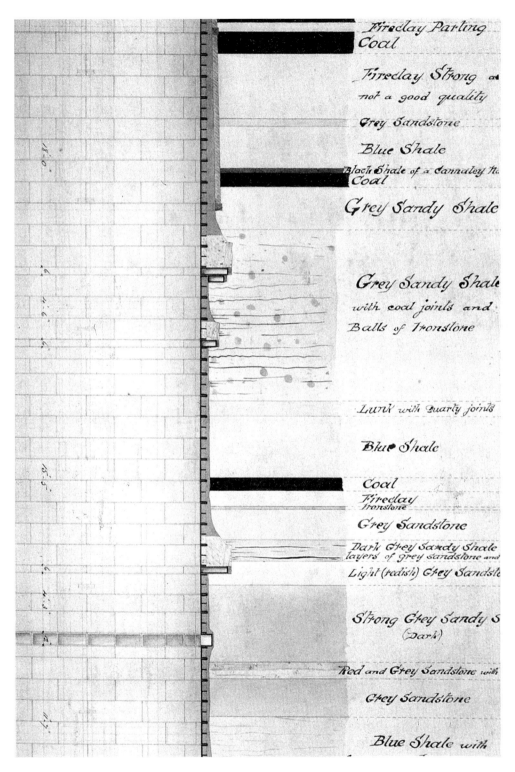

Figure 14: A section of No. 3 shaft; the tubbed shaft is seen passing through the Coal Measures (Photo H.L.Holliday).

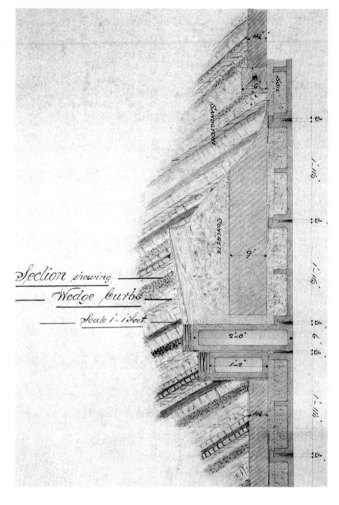

Figure 15: Detail of the Wedge Curbs used in No. 3 shaft (Photo H.L.Holliday). This section graphically illustrates the quality of the Moston Colliery plans (see page 44 for an explanation of these detailed sections).

possible that too much water was getting into the shaft at this point, causing the replacement to be needed.

The large Moston Fault lay some way below, and was known about after 1863 when it can be seen on the Geological Survey map of that year, it being struck at 1,532 feet down. In comparison to the first fault spoken about earlier. The Moston Fault was huge and must have given them much trouble, for it went on down for 84 yards (252 feet) before it had crossed through the shaft wall. This illustrates how near vertical this fault was at the place where it was cut. The fault low down in the new shaft was pure bad luck for Platts, for the fault caused them delays and extra expense in shoring up strongly, for pit bottom was started just yards below the fault. Also because of the fault, the measures were not visible, so in effect they had to find out where the coal was and this was done by exploration tunnels in a southerly direction which struck out into the ground on the upthrow side of the fault.

At last, in August 1887, the two new shafts were ready to wind coal, the first of sixty years production via the Nos 3 and 4 shafts. There were no lasers in use at that time to sink the shafts vertical; any perfection that was built into a shaft then was from the skilled eye of man, assisted by a simple plumb line with a wire radius fixed at the level that the shaft had reached. A straight shaft sunk properly gives no trouble when the two cages are fixed and running and certainly No. 3 was well done, and gave no problems in all its working years.

The fault is like a great tear in the Coal Measures, where the rocks on one side move differently to the rocks on the other. The fault had passed through the shaft by 1,784 feet and 19 feet below this the shaft stopped descending and this became pit bottom, 1,803 feet-10$\frac{1}{2}$ inches below Moston. Except for a small number of exceptions in East Lancashire, the most successful pits of the 19th century were situated west of the River Irwell, which worked easier conditions than the pits nearer to the Pennine Hills. To the east the coals were much more steeply inclined, so working there was usually more difficult for the miners due to the gradient of each coal seam.

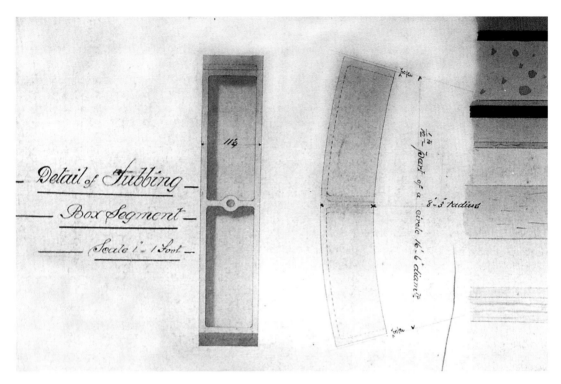

Figure 16: Details of tubbing used in No. 3 shaft, Plate and Box Segments (Photos H.L.Holliday).

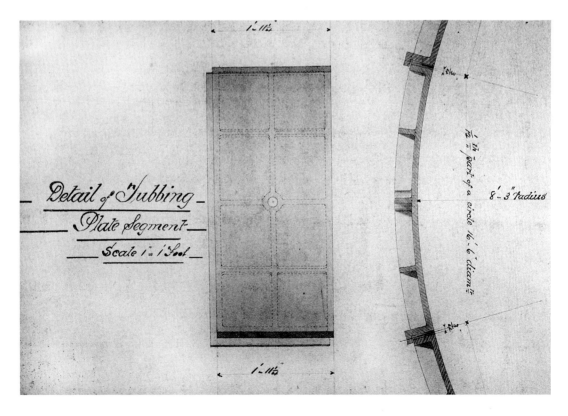

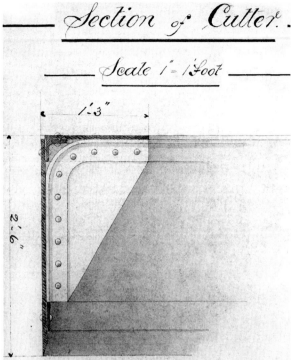

Section of Cutter.

Scale 1" = 1 Foot

1'-3"

2'-6"

Figure 17: The design and dimesions of the cutters set into No. 3 shaft (Photo H.L.Holliday).

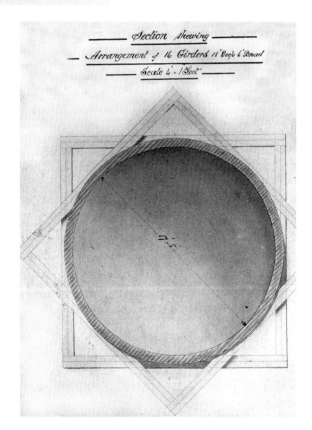

Section shewing

Arrangement of 16 Girders 18 Deep 6 Broad

Scale ¼ = 1 Foot

Figure 18: Details of the 16 girder arrangement in No. 3 shaft to support the great weight of the tubbing in the shaft above (Photo H.L.Holliday) (See pp 44 and 46 for an explanation of this underground arrangement).

11
TWO METHODS OF MINING COAL

As a study to test Platts resolve to have the best in its new pit at Moston, I collected a list of shaft diameters for shafts sunk around 1887 and suggest these speak for themselves.

Date	Name of Pit	1st shaft	2nd shaft	3rd shaft
1866	St Georges	10 feet	10 feet	
1866	Nook Colliery	14 feet	16 feet	
1866	Sandhole	12 feet	12 feet	
1868	Moseley Common	12 feet	12 feet	
1872	Gin Pit.	14 feet	10 feet	
1872	Newtown Pit	16 feet	16 feet	18 feet
1873	Wharton Hall	14 feet	14 feet 3 inch	
1875	Bedford Pit	15 feet	14 feet	
1879	Ashton Moss	16feet	16 feet	
1887	Moston Nos 3,4	18feet (Downcast)	21 feet (Upcast)	
1890	Brackley	14 foot 6 inch	18 feet 6 inch	
1891	Pendleton Colliery	16 feet	16 feet	

In a nutshell, wider shafts meant more coal raised in a given time, two cages rather than one, and more air travelling up the upcast shaft so that more air goes down the downcast resulting in better ventilation. Complaints about Moston being old-fashioned and lacking investment came 50 years later, but in 1887 Moston set the standard for pits in the southeast Lancashire Coalfield. One thing that did let this pit down was that each year its coal had to be cut ever further away from its shafts, but this was not unique to Moston pit, for all pits had this problem as the years went by. Retreat mining would be the only exception and pits that used this method had their own problem. No coal was cut in the first instant when the pit opened, for they initially only set out roadways for their working future, so no profits were made at the beginning of the pit's life.

There are two main methods of mining coal, one in the historic past and the second and later one done in modern times. The earlier one was called mining by "Pillar and Stall", or in some districts "Board & Pillar". Briefly a Stall or Boardway is cut to form a rectangular chamber and all of the coal is taken out, but to support the roof while this takes place, long pillars are left either side. Extra support is given by inserting pit props of wood near the corners of the board and all along the side near to the main roadway. The length of the pillars is the same as the void that has been created by cutting out the coal. Therefore, the

Board most often stops just short of the next cross passage, which is named the headway or alternatively the narrowbay and which is much smaller in size than a standard roadway. The next act can only be described as a robbery, and dangerous it is to execute, especially when seen through our more modern viewpoint for it would never be done this way today.

Quickly, for speed is essential, the miners would now start to cut coal from the body of the pillars, mostly from the sides but also as hollows and even holes cut right through from one side of the pillar to the other. Starting at the furthest end initially, then working towards the main roadway, the miners rob the pillars. Remember, only the pillars hold up the roof and these are being weakened with every blow of the pick. As much coal was taken from the pillars as the miners dare; then a quick retreat is made, for the longer the men rob the pillars, the greater the danger of a roof fall. It has been said that only 50% of the coal was able to be taken out of each pillar safely, so the rest had to be left uncut. Often not enough was left in to support the roof, so after the passing of a few hours or days, the roof came down and any space left open became the goaf where gas lingered and became a danger.

Much later came the new method called "longwall working" and this system had many variations, one to suite any situation below ground. Longwall working is much safer and more efficient for all the coal, for the full height of a seam can be got out successfully. Historically, the Lancashire Coalfield was about the very last of the mining areas to embrace the longwall system; indeed its miners tended to be set against change of any sort. There are no stalls or pillars, only a long clean-cut coal face where the last cut took place. The cutter moves on along the face, the coal is undercut and is then brought down to be shovelled away onto a conveyer belt. Because a long length of face is cut quickly, the roof stands secure for longer.

Any supports to this roof would now be hydraulic roof supports that ensured the safety of the men. After the whole length has been cut, the roof supports are moved forward into the place from where the coal has just been taken, and this process starts again with a new cut. Being a long face cut quickly, when the roof behind starts to come down, it bends in gentle curves rather than snapping and suddenly falling as happened in the days of pillar and stall and so that unknown sudden danger is not present with this newer system. Longwall working can either be by advance or retreat; either will produce a very high percentage of good coal for the pit and this method is much less dangerous than pillar and stall. It used to be said that pillar and stall working was first practised about Newcastle-on-Tyne and that longwall working was first used in the county of Shropshire being called the Shropshire Longwall System. It is fair to say that way back in time Pillar and Stall was the only way to get coal out while supporting the roof above. At Moston, I can only think that their coal cutting was a form of longwall working. Even in the earliest pit, the steep dip in the coal seams would have made the pillars unsafe if they had used pillar and stall working in a number of seams, one seam above another. Ideally irrespective of the distances between coal seams, each pillar should be precisely one above the other.

12
THROUGH THE OLD PIT'S SHAFT PILLAR

It was stated in 1958 that the largest circular mine shaft in Great Britain measured 25 feet in diameter. It says a lot for Platts in sinking a 21 feet diameter shaft as long ago as 1887, seventy years before. The shaft pillar, the undisturbed rock and coal layers that encircled a shaft is a very special place in a coal pit. In modern pits coal is never cut from this pillar, unless it is to make cage room or main haulage tunnels, and these places are always arched with stone or girders.

At Moston, shafts 3-4 are very close together, but the real striking fact is that No. 3 shaft is also quite close to No. 1 shaft of the old flooded pit. Is this huge reservoir of water at 1,000 feet down a risk to the new pit 800 feet lower? I struggled for six months in thought before an understanding came to me about this and just how they sunk a shaft right through the waters without releasing them into the new lower pit. I wonder if those shaft sinkers ever knew what they were sinking beneath? At any place where they sunk a shaft through the old pit workings they would strike a void where the coal had been taken from. This void could be full of water and the shaft that they were sinking would provide a way down for the waters from one pit to the other. Eventually I realised that only one place was safe to put a shaft through, and this was the shaft pillar of No. 1 shaft, for here the coal was intact and in a way would act like the cork in a bottle, a way down without disturbing the waters. This then explains why No. 3 is as close as 200 yards from No. 1 shaft and why No. 4 shaft is only 30 yards away from No. 3, both placed near the edge of the shaft pillar of No. 1 pit, the shaft close by Nuthurst Railway Bridge.

Nos 3 and 4 shafts of this later pit were accessible from St Mary's Road, the pit road running quite straight until it entered the pit yard (see Figure 39 for a plan of the pit top layout). One of the later pits' regular customers would have been Moston Mill. This is borne out by the fact that railway lines from No. 1 pit yard (the old pit), crossed over Nuthurst Road near to the bend and these continued up the Millfield, making coal deliveries easy by the use of the Moston Pit locomotive. At this place, running parallel with the lines, a small tunnel (a manway) crossed under the road. I never knew its real purpose, but think it was for the smooth running of the coal train, perhaps to allow the man who changed the points a safe way back after the train had gone through. These developments started with the coming of the first locomotive soon after 1900, but Moston always had its own engine right up to the closure in 1950. I saw these things myself in my youth and well remember the weigh bridge at this same stretch of roadway with its big wide window so the operator could see to weigh the coal and its conveyance. (This can be seen in Figure 21, right hand side).

When kibbles were used in early pit shafts, they were able to negotiate an out-of-line shaft, for being made after the pattern of a basket, were flexible and so were able to take the knocks and bumps even if the men travelling on them couldn't. The coming of cages gave great trouble if the shaft wasn't perfectly straight, and because it was impossible to straighten a bent shaft, it would have to be fitted with a smaller cage to pass the bad place safely. Conductors were essential for a smooth cage run, these being smooth wires hung down the length of the shaft and fixed in the sump below to a very heavy weight which kept the wire tight, the weights being named cheese weights. By 1887 a cage or cages were the norm and because Moston's pillar had been left intact, the new shafts were incredibly straight and there were no problems with winding the twin cages in No. 3 shaft. Early cages had no gates fitted, but it was just a matter of time before this addition came about, and one would have thought its need would have been realised earlier. Also cage tops were absent, not thought necessary in those early days, but after a few accidents with falling objects, a deflecting cover in metal was fitted and from that time onwards it saved many lives. It goes without saying that Moston Colliery had these two items fitted at an early stage.

On the shaft section for No. 3 shaft are clearly drawn, but only in pencil not in ink, a pair of "balance bobs". This L-shaped arrangement transferred a horizontal movement into a vertical one, or put another way, it changed forward movement from an engine into up and down movement for the pump rods that went down the side of the shaft. In the deep, water-filled sump, 1,840 feet below the surface, the pump would have worked connected to the bottom pump rod. The water would have been driven up iron pipes possibly into cisterns fitted at various heights up the shaft, and secondary pumps did further lifts from these cisterns until the water spilled out into the pit reservoir. Improvements were coming along all the time, so I have a suspicion that this old fashioned pumping system did not in the end get used.

Newer things, non-return valves, and direct acting pumps, were just starting to be used, so the need for pump rods was coming to an end. Electricity was the newer power source that was taking over in the coal mines. If I am correct, instead of cisterns in various places up the shaft as a way of lifting water up to the surface, now there would be a succession of electric pumps fixed into the pipe-work at various heights in the shaft. Perhaps the balance bobs were drawn in at an early stage of the planning, but in the three years of sinking, the new type of pumping was decided upon. To bear this out, on the shaft section for No. 3 shaft, a Pumping Chamber is drawn at 623 feet down, and there are no signs of any pump rods. So it looks like the old system of pumping out mine waters was superseded by the new style pumps that were driven by electricity in 1887 for the new pit shafts Nos 3 and 4.

Water pipes are shown coming up into this chamber from below, merging and interchanging before proceeding up towards the surface. The chamber at 623 feet below the surface measured 10 feet high and

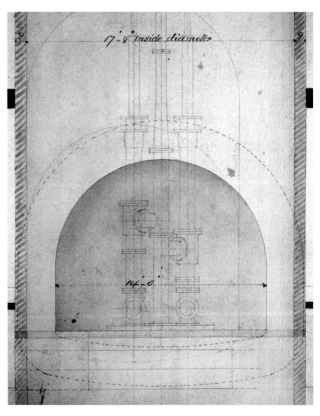

Figure 19: The pumping chamber at 623 feet down in No. 3 shaft.

was 14 feet wide. I suspect that a second chamber exists below at 1,230 feet down, but this has not been found on any plan. It is certain that any form of pumping from 1,800 feet down would require at least three lifts to bring water successfully to the surface whatever method was used.

In this chapter I have tried to point out why the shaft pillar is of such importance in a coal mine, and especially so at Moston with the old flooded pit ever present above. Here is a short story of another Lancashire pit that had trouble in its pillar; this trouble was so serious that it closed this pit down forever. Outwood Colliery which lay between Radcliffe and Kearsley, northwest of Manchester, lay to the east of the Irwell Valley Fault. It was a major colliery by size with steeply dipping coal seams, though not as steep as at Moston. In 1929 the pit was taken over by the Manchester Collieries group, but unfortunately they drew a short straw on this purchase. Soon an underground fire ignited and slowly ate its way into the heart of the shaft pillar. This then so weakened the underground workings that the shaft at its centre collapsed in on itself and disappeared down the hole. The heat from below was intense, and was drawn up where the shaft had been; like a blast-furnace. This heat soon bent the struts of the headgear at the surface and it leaned over and disappeared into the hole that had once been the pit shaft. In falling, it dragged down with it the cage winding cable that was still attached at both ends. It was said that this wire cut through the engine house wall as if it had been fashioned out of butter. The moral of this true story must be, look after your shaft pillar for everything about the pit stands upon it.

Figure 20: A poor quality photograph of Pits 3-4 at full steam in 1915 (Photo reproduced with kind permission of Fr Brian Seale).

Figure 21: Moston Best Coal" won first prize at the Newton Heath Parade of 1928. Those huge lumps were blocks of Roger Seam Coal. (Photo T. Holliday, taken across Nuthurst Road towards the weighbridge; the pit stands behind it).

13

THE INFLUENCE OF
THE MOSTON FAULT

The Moston Fault was a further piece of bad luck for the owners of the pit, Platt Brothers Holdings. The initial choice of site for the two new shafts was governed purely by the area which the old shaft pillar covered. There was little to see on the surface; the fault was not visible due to the glacial drift being thick at that point. All coalfields are effected by faults, sometimes only in a single coal seam, but many pit shafts must have been sunk through faults. Once the fault has passed through the width of the shaft, coal seams reappear but may not be recognised or indeed may not be the ones expected. The Moston Fault runs roughly northwest by southeast with the upthrow side on the west; thus south was the way to go safely, so as not to mine coal beneath flooded workings of the old pit. In seeking coal seams, they would have to search beyond this fault into unknown ground. The fault took 252 feet to move through the shaft, from 1,532 feet down to 1,784 feet, this proving how near vertical the fault was. It would have been full of ground up, disturbed rock and the expected sequence of coal seams in their turn was lost, below the point where the fault crossed the shaft.

Much strengthening was done below the fault in the lower part of the shaft and this added to Platts already high costs; indeed I do not know why shaft bottom was set at just 19 feet below the faulted part of the shaft. It may be that worries over finance stopped any further deepening of the shaft at that point and the big question remained, where is the coal? I can't say for certain that shaft bottom was on the upthrow side of the fault, but certainly if one walked along the main roadway from the pit bottom in a westerly direction, you passed a fault in the right-hand roadway wall. I did not see this when accompanying my father, but my friend and ex-pit deputy Thomas Allen told me of this fact, and my imagination has to provide the picture.

Thomas also said that just feet from this place, near to the fault, was a superb coal of 4 feet thick, black like bitumen; he thought it was an anthracite. I wonder if the movement during the faulting had caused heating to make changes in the coal. Regrettably it was never mined or followed by the miners, for it was at too steep an angle to set timbers in, and shall always remain a mystery for we never knew the name of this coal seam. He went on to say that experiments had been done on the coal to see what its properties were, and it was described as an exceptionally hot coal when burned; perhaps the most striking thing was its appearance, jet black and very shiny. I never saw these features with my father for we always set off from shaft bottom in an easterly direction. I never saw the fault or the stables, and so never got to the big wooden doors. If one could look along the fault, in a northwest direction, the left-hand wall is called the footwall, the right-hand wall being the hanging wall.

To get away from the waters above in the old pit, and to seek out the coal seams that were still at this stage unknown, exploration tunnels were started in a southerly direction; finding the coal early was an urgent priority for Platts in 1887. Incidentally I now believe that at the time of the flooding, the details of the Moston Fault were known about, for it is shown on the first geological map of 1863.

The footwall side of the Moston Fault, in moving upwards during its greatest turmoil many millions of years ago, brought up from deep down two unexpected coal seams along with their associated measures. These two coals were found beyond the fault wall, one within three years of the re-opening in 1890, and the second and deepest one 30 years later in about 1917. The first of these two coals had started to be worked. It had been called the Platt Seam to celebrate what was their first piece of good luck. Soon it was recognised that the Platt seam of Moston correlated with the "Oldham Great Mine" of other districts. This was a fair coal about Oldham, but was spoiled at many pits by numerous bands of stone called dirt partings that ran through the seam; five distinct bands were known in some places up at some Oldham pits. At Moston, however, these stone bands had gone and it was a fine coal, 3 feet 2 inches minimum thickness. It was first found not very far from the shaft bottom; this then became the second coal seam opened out, the first being the Roger Coal, called Big Seam at this pit. Platt Seam had been displaced upwards by the Moston Fault 720 feet from its original horizon, and would have lain 2,523 feet below Moston without the action of this fault. This also applies to the other coal from even deeper down, called the Black Seam, i.e. the Black Seam of Oldham.

It was about 1917 when the management at Moston needed to find a new coal to open up for the next few years work. They decided that the famous Black Mine coal of Oldham was not too far below the Platt Seam, and so work started in a very determined way to find this coal. Two special tunnels had been started as soon as the shaft No. 3 was finished in 1887, one from the level of the Platt Seam, which was called the Platt Tunnel, and a second one from a somewhat higher place starting in the Mary Mine workings (see later). This second exploration tunnel was called the Hardman Tunnel, and was situated under Broadway, but heading a little west of south towards Failsworth. The Platt Tunnel ran under the later Ferranti's factory in line with St Mary's Road, but nearer to the railway line, and headed for Newton Heath. This tunnel was where the search for Black Mine coal started, and it was found from a tunnel that was heading north off the Platt Tunnel. The Black Seam had also been displaced by the fault by 720 feet and its true position would have been about 2,793 feet below Moston without the fault's action. Black Mine coal was very important at Moston in the late 1920s when my father first came to Moston to work, as can be seen from his photograph (Figure 31).

One reason for the need to open out new coal seams at Moston was because, in looking for others, new ground was being explored. I have to say that they did sail a little near to the wind when taking coal from those last two seams (Platt and Black) for the northward passage where they found the coal was just about under the waters of the Old Pit above.

Nos 3 and 4 are completed in August 1887
The height above sea level was 314.30 feet at the surface
N 53° 30' 54" W 2° 10' 30"
In 1946 the pit telephone number was Failsworth 2603

Shaft No. 3 (downcast) sunk by Platt Bros Holdings between 1884-1887
Glacial Drift down to170 feet 10 inches
Total depth of shaft 1,803 feet 10$\frac{1}{2}$ inches
Shaft Diameter 18 feet
Big Seam (Roger Coal) at 1,298 feet 4$\frac{1}{2}$ inches down
Normal vertical section to 1,532 feet then faulted ground down to 1,784 feet
N. C. B. shaft reference No. 30

Shaft No. 4 (upcast) sunk by Platt Bros Holdings between 1884-1887
Shaft Diameter 21 feet
Depth of shaft 675 feet
N. C. B. shaft reference No. 31(?)

No. 3 shaft was the main winding shaft, and being the downcast had no problems with firedamp, so was safer in operation. Its cages travelled up and down the shaft at 88 feet per second (which is about 60 miles per hour maximum velocity, but a little slower when men were carried) and the engine was powered by steam. I can still remember the startled, fearful looks on the faces of some classmates as they hurtled down to the bottom of No. 3 on a day's visit, just prior to us all leaving school to find work. I was an old hand at riding in the cage, so I knew to keep swallowing every so often as the cage descends at speed. Changes in atmospheric pressure did painful things to young ear drums in a fast descent. It may be possible to get used to this pain in time, but never on a first descent, and it is not easy to keep swallowing all of the way down. Twelve kids eagerly rushed out into the light at the bottom as the cage gate was opened; eleven had drawn pallid faces and popping eyes, while I, the twelfth, had a normal coloured face and a little smile, for I had been that way before.

Big or Roger Seam started producing	1887
Platt Seam	1890
Mary Seam	1896
Major Seam	1898
Black Seam	1920
Foxholes 1	1940
Foxholes 2	1940
Colonel Seam	1940

In addition H.M. Inspector of Mines (John Gerrard's tables for 1896) stated that Colonel Seam as well as Foxholes were being worked in 1896; these were then re-worked in 1940 at a different district of the pit.

14

THE COAL SEAMS MINED AT MOSTON COLLIERY

In giving details of the coal seams that were mined, it is essential to understand that although I show them in their true positions and their depths down in the shaft, this was not the place where the coal was taken from. It would have been totally unbusiness-like to stop the cage at as many as eight different landings in an 1,800 foot shaft, to put coal in trucks into the cage to wind up to the surface. Granted, perhaps only four were being worked at any one given date, but it was not done that way for the coal would always be backing up at four levels in the shaft. As this pit was not a rise pit anymore, all of those coals that crossed through the shaft higher up, would eventually come down to the same level as shaft bottom. To mine them required only that a gallery went out into the right area, to intercept the coal, and from that point coal mining started. There were 8 coal seams mined in all, but I can only give 5 of these accurately, as to where they occurred in the shaft, and the lower three would only be a rough estimate because of the fault. The five are shown in the order that they were met with in the No. 3 shaft:

Moston pit name	Universal names for coals	Thickness of coal	Depth down in shaft
Major seam	Old Jet Amber	3ft 6ins	1,088ft 6ins
Colonel Seam	Ashton Great Seam	3ft 8½ins	1,213ft 11ins
Big Seam (Roger)	The Roger Coal	6ft 3 ins+9½ins	1,298ft 4½ins
Foxholes 1	Top Furness (Devil)	2ft 6ins	1,386ft-8ins
Foxholes 2	Lr Furness Seam	3ft 7½ins	1,403ft 9ins
Mary Seam	Fairbottom Seam	3ft 7ins	?
Platt Seam	Oldham Great seam	3ft 2ins	?
Black Seam	Oldham Black seam	3ft 9ins	?

N.B. Foxholes Seam at Moston is not the same as the Foxholes Seam at Ashton.
Mary Mine at Moston is not the same coal as Mary Seam at Ashton.

The same names for different coal seams happens often in the Lancashire coalfield. Tonks *et al.* (1930) states:

"in addition to the different sets of names in use in the eastern and western coalfields, there are often within each area, several names for any one seam. This multiplicity of nomenclature could be caused by the heavy faulting that the Coal Measures have undergone, and to the consequent splitting of the coal seams into districts separated by large faults. Very often the names only refer directly or indirectly to the thickness of the seams. Not only do the names come to be used for coals widely separated in the vertical succession, but as the seams vary in thickness from place to place, new names are of necessity used."

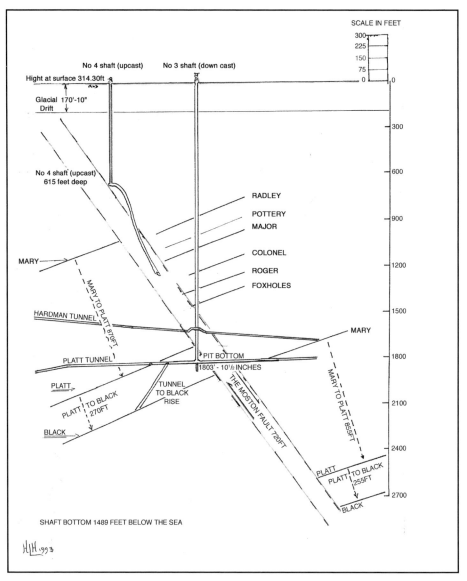

Figure 22: A Moston Colliery Section Of Shafts Nos 3,4.
Section showing shafts, coals and faults.

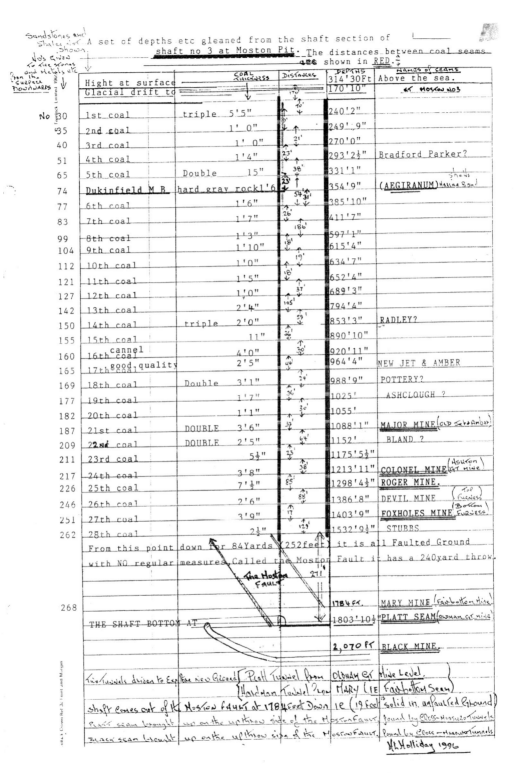

A set of depths etc gleaned from the shaft section of
shaft no 3 at Moston Pit. The distances between coal seams
are shown in RED.

Sandstones and Shales not Shown.
Nos Given to the stones and Metals etc from the Surface Downwards

		COAL THICKNESS	Distances	DEPTHS	NAMES OF SEAMS Above the sea.
	Hight at surface			314'30Ft	at MOSTON NO3
	Glacial drift to		10'	170'10"	
No 30	1st coal	triple 5'5"	6'	240'2"	
35	2nd coal	1' 0"	21'	249'9"	
40	3rd coal	1' 0"	23'	270'0"	
51	4th coal	1'4"	38'	293'2½"	Bradford Parker?
65	5th coal	Double 15"	23'	331'1"	
74	Dukinfield M.B.	hard gray rock1'6"	54' 31'	354'9"	(AEGIRANUM) Halling Sand
77	6th coal	1'6"	26'	385'10"	
83	7th coal	1'7"	186'	411'7"	
99	8th coal	1'3"	18'	597'1"	
104	9th coal	1'10"	19'	615'4"	
112	10th coal	1'0"	18'	634'7"	
121	11th coal	1'5"	37'	652'4"	
127	12th coal	1'0"	105'	689'3"	
142	13th coal	2'4"	59'	794'4"	
150	14th coal	triple 2'0"	36'	853'3"	RADLEY?
155	15th coal	11"	30'	890'10"	
160	16th coal cannel	4'0"		920'11"	
165	17th coal good quality	2'5"	24'	964'4"	NEW JET & AMBER
169	18th coal	Double 3'1"	36'	988'9"	POTTERY?
177	19th coal	1'7"	30'	1025'	ASHCLOUGH ?
182	20th coal	1'1"	33'	1055'	
187	21st coal	DOUBLE 3'6"	64'	1088'1"	MAJOR MINE (old Jet & Amber)
209	22nd coal	DOUBLE 2'5"	23'	1152'	BLAND ?
211	23rd coal	5½"	38'	1175'5½"	
217	24th coal	3'8"	85'	1213'11"	COLONEL MINE (Ashton Jet mine)
226	25th coal	7'½"	89'	1298'4½"	ROGER MINE.
246	26th coal	2'6"	17'	1386'8"	DEVIL MINE (Top Furness)
251	27th coal	3'9"	129'	1403'9"	FOXHOLES MINE (Bottom Furness)
262	28th coal	2½"		1532'9½"	STUBBS

From this point down for 84 Yards (252feet) it is all Faulted Ground
with NO regular measures. Called the Moston Fault it has a 240yard throw.

The Moston Fault   27'

268				1784Ft.	MARY MINE (Fairbottom Mine)
THE SHAFT BOTTOM AT				1803'10½"	PLATT SEAM (Oldham Gt mine)
				2,070Ft	BLACK MINE.

Two Tunnels driven to Explore new Ground { Platt Tunnel from OLDHAM Gt Mine Level.
{ Hardman Tunnel from MARY (IE Fairbottom Seam)

Shaft comes out of the MOSTON FAULT at 1784 Feet Down ie (19 feet solid in unfaulted Ground)
Platt seam brought up on the upthrow side of the Moston Fault Found by Cross-Measure Tunnels
Black seam brought up on the upthrow side of the Moston Fault. Found by Cross-Measure Tunnels

H.L.Holliday 1996

Figure 23: A table showing Rock Layers and Coals in No. 3 shaft down to the
point at which it hit the Moston Fault 1533 feet below the surface.

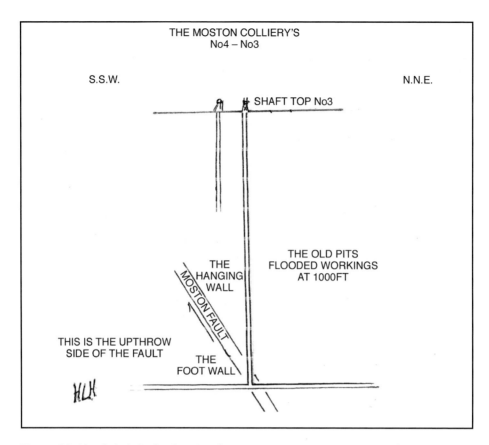

Figure 24: Nos 3 & 4 shafts showing features and the Platt and the Hardman Tunnels.

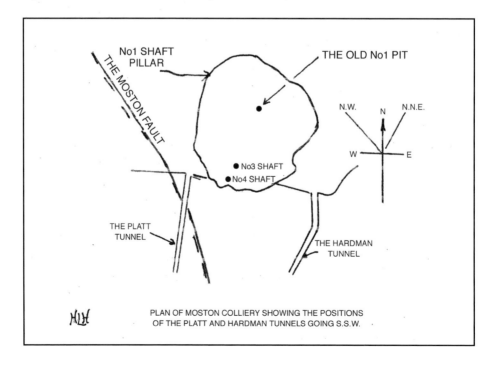

The Platt and Hardman tunnels remain something of a mystery to me for they were not mentioned when I was down in the pit. But after the year of 1887 in the new pit, these two roadways were tunnels into the future, the keys to finding the coal, required to help pay for the great investment already spent. Success or failure of the pit depended upon these two roadways. I did walk down the Hardman Tunnel on each of my visits with my father; perhaps the nearer to our time, the less this name was used so that it slowly went from man's memory. Thomas Allen (ex-Pit Deputy) said he had never heard it called the Hardman Tunnel.

Both roadways set off into new unexplored ground and in doing so had to pass through the Moston Fault. On the upthrow side the coal was located and turned out to be the promised land for this pit and its workers.

Figure 25 shows the influence of the Moston Fault at No. 3 shaft. Column A shows the measures as found at shaft sinking in 1887, while column B shows the measures as they would have been, if there had been no fault. The coals in the faulted block on the western side of the Moston Fault, have been upthrown by the fault's influence and so are now at a higher level relative to the next block. east of the fault, however, not much movement can be seen; the result of these movements is that when the shaft sunk through the fault, some of the expected coal seams were missing entirely, carried up to higher horizon.

The following are the missing coals at Moston's No. 3 shaft:

1. Equivalent to the Ashton district's Foxhole or Mary Seam (not the same as Moston's of the same name).
2. Cannel Seam or Town Lane
3. Top Shuttles Seam
4. Bottom Shuttles Seam.
5. Higher Chamber Seam
6. Lower Chamber Seam
7. Foggs Seam.

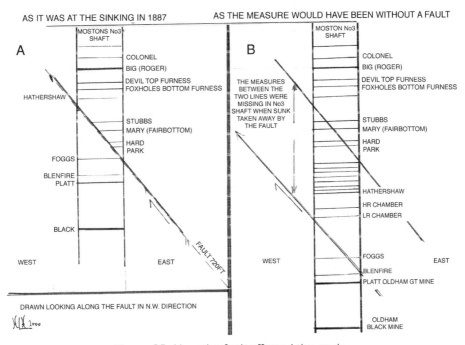

Figure 25: How the fault affected the coals.

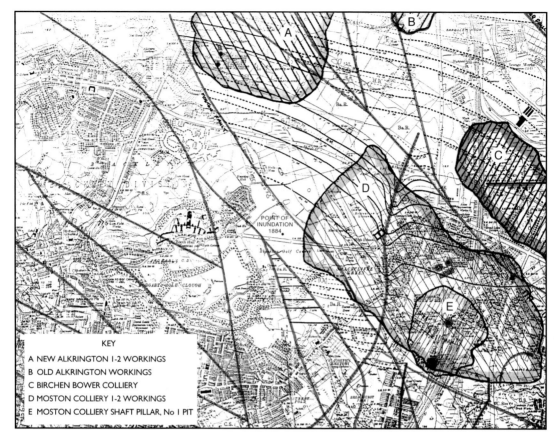

KEY

A NEW ALKRINGTON 1-2 WORKINGS
B OLD ALKRINGTON WORKINGS
C BIRCHEN BOWER COLLIERY
D MOSTON COLLIERY 1-2 WORKINGS
E MOSTON COLLIERY SHAFT PILLAR, No 1 PIT

Figure 26: A Geological Survey Map date 1932, showing area from which coal was mined with special emphasis on the faults that cut the Coal Measures. Extract courtesy of the British Geological Survey.

15

THE MANAGEMENT AND

THEIR HELPERS

At the time that the new pit started producing, a lot of the offices in and around the pit had names that are unfamiliar to us today, such as overlookers or underlookers, putters and hewers. However it is beyond the scope of this book to use or explain these terms even if I knew them all, so here using more modern names is an explanation of the management structure. The overall control of the smooth running of the pit rested with the General Manager. He would have to answer to the Board of Directors somewhere in Oldham, but his days were filled at the pit with hiring and firing, designating responsibilities to others and generally being in control of things up top. This Moston Pit being the key part of the coal production for Platts, and now able to supply coals of quality and also in quantity, was in effect the power source that made their engineering works such a great industry in and about Oldham. Now, only Moston could supply enough coal to keep the coke furnaces working, and this had been the reason that they bought the pit in the first place.

Underground was the domain of the Under-Manager; he had offices down below as well as on the surface and was in constant touch with his deputies who had a sector or district of the pit to administer. The Under-Manager had to keep production high and plan the pit's next move below ground, always planning ahead before a sector ran out of coal. He used the pit's maps, and had to be something of a geologist as well; finally, safety in the pit was for him to administer. One step below was the Overman; a willing Overman could warn his Under-Manager of impending troubles because he moved through the roadways in a regular fashion and could spot changes since he last went that way. Below the Overman were the Pit Deputies. If you became a Deputy you had got one foot on the ladder to promotion.

The Deputies were the link between the management and the ordinary miner. They tested for gas before the miners' shift started, much like the penitent of old, but using more modern methods. Many times a day they would test and re-test for gas, but to be truthful I consider Moston to have been one of the less gassy pits in the Oldham coalfield. However, Moston did have good, vigorous ventilation, and this goes some way to lessen the risk of a gas explosion, and it is believed that the pit never had one. The Pit Deputies were the safety officers in the pit, checking lamps, measuring airflow and pressures in various places below ground. When blasting charges were fired by the shot firer (often a Pit Deputy at Moston I am told) he had to walk from area to area to accomplish this. The Pit Deputies had the given power to stop all work below ground, and to send the men out if they deemed anything as unsafe or dangerous. Really the Deputies were the eyes and ears of the pit, reporting anything that may bring trouble into the workings.

It was the law that canaries had to be kept at all coal pits in the event of a build up of gas. They would be called for by telephone and carried down to where they were required, and with a smaller percentage of gas than would kill a man, they would simply fall off their

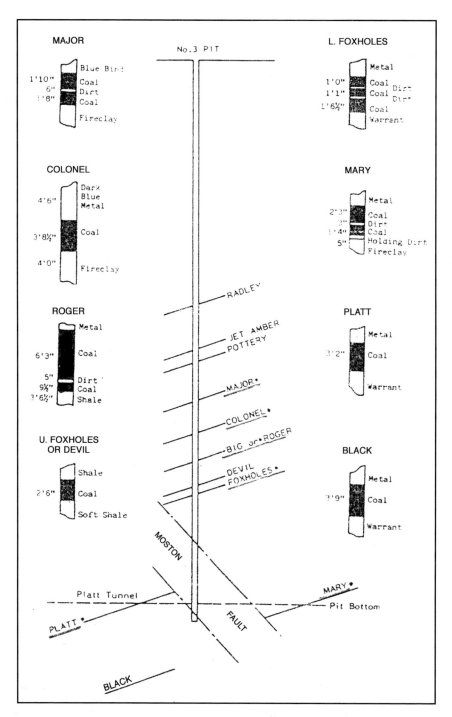

Figure 27: Details of the coals mined at Moston Colliery's later pit. Shows the seams that were mined at Moston as well as their details. The shaft section shows the coals position as each seam crossed No. 3 shaft. It goes without saying that the coals were not mined from the place they were seen in the shaft, but each coal came down to shaft bottom at some point and so finding each coal seam as it reachèd the level of the haulage roads below was a fairly uncomplicated business. Higher coals in the shaft took longer to reach the bottom than did the lower coals.

perches, and at that sign the men would get out. The afterdamp after a firedamp explosion was another reason the canaries were kept in readiness at the pit. They were kept in cages ready for the call of duty and lived in the timekeeper's office.

One day, I remember clearly, being taken by my father into one of the offices, and there, standing in the corner behind the door, was a rack full of sticks. These were called 'Deputy's sticks', and unlike a walking stick, had a round knob at the top. All types of mines had a stock of these, for they were not unique to coal mines; metal mines all over Britain used them, for they were a symbol, a sign of office, a stick to show status or experience to the working miners in their place of toil. The Manager going round the pit yard would take one, the Under-Manager certainly would use one and also his Overmen, and the Pit Deputies as well, and any important visitors who were going to descend the mine (see Figure 29 of two visiting members of Parliament both carrying Deputy's sticks). I see some similarity between the Deputy's stick of the pit, and the mace or ceremonial staff in the Council Chamber.

Figure 28: The Author aged 5, taken in a garden on Broadway, with the pit in the background. This Photo was taken in 1938. See page 97. (Photo T. Holliday).

Figure 29: "In Miners Kit". Title from a newspaper cutting, date unknown. Mr Hamilton Kerr M.P. and Miss Irene Ward M.P. for Walsend visited the Moston Colliery this morning and are seen ready for the descent. Mr T Holliday on the left, hands Miss Ward a safety lamp; the third person from the left is Mr H Richford the pit's General Manager. Note that the visitors have been given a Deputy's stick to help them below with their walking.

Figure 30: The Winding Drum for No. 3 shaft taken in 1929 (Photo T. Holliday).

Figure 31: The Black Mine coal face in 1929 (Photo T. Holliday).

Figure 32: The Winding Engine for No. 3 shaft (Photo T. Holliday).

Figure 33: The Air Compressor for the pit, which stood in No. 3 engine house (Photo T. Holliday 1929.) I think that the maker for this piece of equipment was Ingersol.

16
THE PROBLEM OF CRUSH

During 1928 and 1929 my father, Thomas Holliday, was much concerned at Moston Colliery with the problem of crush in the lower levels of the mine. Whether this concern came from a task that he had been set by the Mine Manager, or just in his own interests, I do not know. All I know is that he took a series of photographs in the depths of the pit, and after some time went by, took a second set in the same places as previously and so was able to see changes due to crush. Everything deep in the mine was either black or white, including the colour of his film, but these photos have been treasured by me all these years and if re-printed are as crisp as if they were taken only yesterday. I can only assume that his purpose was to see for himself how quickly crush comes on into a newly cut roadway and what, if anything, can be done to stop, or lesson, the deformation of this roadway over time.

Crush is the word used to describe the damage that the combined weight of the rocks above the roadway do to that roadway; in the case at Moston there was at least 2,000 feet of overlying rock, which is indescribably heavy. In a coal pit the area of space from where the coal is taken is allowed to crush down after the coal has gone, and this area is called the goaf or gob. Waste rock materials can be stacked into this space as the workers move on to cut more coal, but it is inevitable that the roof will fall whatever man does, for crush is an irresistible force. The haulage roadway's, however, where the coal will be brought up to the shaft and so to the surface, must stand and resist for many years, and then stand some more. Things can be done to lesson the damage, such as leaving the coal intact along the sides of the roadway, or building extra supports with stone along its length. If this passage deforms with the pressure then work has to be done to keep it open, and man-hours used upon it. If steel girders are used they can usually take the weight better and for longer, especially if the floor below the coal is strong and solid, but crush is relentless driven by the weight of the rock above.

The first photo (Fig. 34) shows a cross-measure tunnel running on the horizontal from Platt Mine to Black Mine; there are no coals near and a cross-measure tunnel means a tunnel through solid rock. Father's second photograph (Fig. 35) is along the same passage 12 months later and no crush had occurred; even a wood propped area had not moved at all. His third and fourth photos (Figs 36 and 37) were taken deep down in the pit, in a roadway dipping at 1 in 3, supported by steel arches through packed waste. The coal seam had already been taken out and the space had been filled with waste rock. It took my father 18 months to get back to that same spot to take the fourth photograph (Fig. 37). It shows great signs of crush from the weight of rock above; the girders stand secure, but the timber packing behind the arches had buckled and broken. Because those girders stood secure, a soft floor had begun to creep up into the area of the roadway, and the trucks can only run tilted on uneven rails. More work for the maintenance men?

Figure 34: A cross-measure roadway from Platt to Black Mine running through strong solid ground supported by steel arching 6 feet by 6 feet. Photo T Holliday 1929.

Figure 35: The same roadway after 12 months showing no crush (Photo T.Holliday).

Figure 36: A roadway dipping at 1 in 3 through packed waste, steel arching 6 feet by 6 feet. The coal had already gone from this section of the mine. Photo T Holliday 1929.

Figure 37: The same roadway after 18 months, showing great effects of crush; the timber buckles behind the girders, and a soft floor has risen up to tilt the coal trucks (Photo T. Holliday).

When taken down the mine all the timber used for propping up the roof carries fungal spores in its outer bark, which have the potential to reduce the props' strength and also the length of its useful life. Timber was recovered and re-used as coal cutting moved relentlessly onwards into new areas. The conditions down below, being warm and damp, were ideal for the fungal spores to grow and thrive, so timber really had only a short life down a pit. Platt Brothers, being quite forward-looking and being themselves in the metal working trade, decided at an early stage to use girders made from steel to stabilise a roadway through the rock. Timber packing still had to be used, as well as stone packs and waste rock, to give extra strength near any edges or corners. Thin sawn wood was even more open to attack from the fungus and so its life was limited by this same factor. However, it was safer and much easier to change these packings from time to time than to reset new wood pit props through an old roadway.

Going back to my father's photographs (Figures 34-37) I suppose his most important observation was that if the rock, or the rock and coal, was left *in situ* while the gallery was cut through, then that roadway would stand secure for very many years. If on the other hand the roadway being driven ran through an area from which the coal had already gone, all would be done to put back strength and to secure a strong roadway by packing with stone and waste; the roadway is in effect made through an old goaf. But in a year or two, however tight it had been packed, because the coal had gone, the roadway would be showing signs of settlement, and crush effects would be visible for all to see. The girders would give in time, perhaps a long time, and sometimes the floor would creep up into the roadway space spoiling the levels of the rails. The maintenance men would have to come in to correct things so the trucks could run level again along the roadway. I expect father learned more than just this in 1929. He never showed me these photographs in his lifetime, nor did he ever speak of them to me. It is therefore obvious that I am assuming this story from his photos, and after his death when they became mine, I realised that these four photographs were but a small incident in his working life. Floor heave (the problem of the floor rising up into the space of the roadway) is due to the softness of the floor or hardness of roof rocks and has little to do with crush or the great depth of the pit bottom.

Some thoughts about crush

Man built his Cathedrals and thus enclosed a holy space in stone. This was then an extension of heaven here upon the Earth. Man did a good job. When man removed coal from the rocks of the Earth, he was removing those pillars on which the surface stood. He then put waste rock in the void. Man did a poor job.

The Earth could not live comfortably with these open spaces inside her, so she set to and filled them in using her power called crush. She did a very good job.

17
VERMIN AND THE PIT PONIES

I was informed that all collieries had their fair share of pests and creepy-crawly creatures that inhabited the dark places in the depth of the mine. They managed somehow without light and were capable of eating just about anything that came their way, for out of their true element necessity forced them to eat whatever and whenever they could. Many a pit man has lost his food in an instant, simply because he put down his food for a second in order to take a drink. The introduction of the snap tin was the invention that let a man eat his lunch himself, this being simply a tin with a tight fitting lid. Previous to this the men had to tie their food to a high prop or beam in the vain hope that these creatures could not climb, but in truth they lived in and on those pit props. The invisible hoards that infested walls and roof were not often seen unless a light was suddenly switched on in a dark place. Crickets were there along with cockroaches and these two did not get along very well; I was told it was "dog eat dog". Many kinds of beetles were there as well, but these did not last long for they apparently were somewhere near the bottom of the food chain. All these creatures it is said were carried down with the timber possibly hiding in the roughness of the bark.

Worse still were the rats and the mice, which came down with the hay and the bedding, which was destined for the pit ponies in their underground stables. It is said that no pit had both, for the rats would eat up all of the mice, and at Moston pit, the rats were in complete control. I used to imagine that one rat somehow fell down the shaft and survived, only to find another rat of the opposite sex waiting with open arms, but the answer is far simpler than that. Rats would eat anything, even the heaps that fell between the rails after a pit pony had passed. At first because of man's presence in the pit bottom, the rats were not often seen, but it was known they were there for occasionally a squeak would be heard or a snapping sound as a rat moved across a piece of fallen shale. The goaf area was never entered by the miners even at times of real bodily emergency. Therefore a miner was forced to use the side of the roadway and for his own safety, must listen for the sound of trucks coming so as not to place himself in danger. The goaf was the area from which coal had been taken, and now, if still standing, stood totally unpropped.

Cracking sounds could be heard at times, as the stresses came down onto the roof of the newly vacated goaf. The rats lived totally in the roadways for here lay the source of their food. Stone or waste rock would be stowed in the goaf in the vain hope that it would hold up the roof for longer, but Mother Nature packs rock much tighter than man can. Inevitably the coal cutting moves forward creating newer goafs, but the vermin stay close to man in their roadways, for without man and the ponies the vermin would die. Gas can collect in the closing down goaf, and if a fire starts up, it is most difficult to deal with, for it is not a safe place for man to penetrate into, especially when fighting a fire.

The truth about the rats is this; it only requires one pregnant female to start a colony and the whole circle of life is initiated, be it in the streets above, or the roadways below ground. They came down to shaft bottom, probably wrapped up in a warm bale of hay or straw, which was meant for the comfort of the pit ponies in their stables. I was told that the moment that the ponies shift finished, they were unhitched from the trucks that they were pulling and that they simply set off on their own to the stable, where the "Ostler" was waiting to wash off their legs with a water hose. Then after they walked into their own section of the stable he fed them and they settled down for their rest period. They would get their coats brushed daily, but that job may have been done before their shift started after they had rested. [If this part of my story seems to flit about between rats and mice and the pit ponies, then it is because they are inextricably linked together in a web that spelt problems and trouble for the pit.]

The ponies, were much loved members of the work force. Each pony had its own "Putter" and the ponies recognised his voice as they moved about in the dark roadways of the pit pulling a number of coal trucks, full ones to the shaft and empties back to the coal face again. At least once a year the ponies were brought up to the surface for a holiday, to frolic in the pit field that I remember well. It was at the side of St Mary's Road where the miners' houses, built for Bradford Colliery in about 1964, now stand. Vets attended any ponies that were unwell or that had sustained an injury from a falling rock and they were re-shod at very regular intervals. After some time down in the depths, the ponies became totally used to their situation, but make no mistake, they also remembered what it was like above ground in the warmth of the sun. If a pony received a bad injury in the pit, a feeling of sadness affected the men, and they talked about it just like we talk about the weather today. The ponies' holiday up top in the pit field may not have started off too well. In pits that only had small diameter shafts the ponies had to travel the shaft slung underneath the cage and hung in a kind of hammock or harness. However this was not the case at Moston No. 3, for the cage was big and spacious, and so they would probably just walk quietly into the cage in twos. In their field they lay about with their bruised and battered legs warming in the sun, but were full of joy to be there.

Some general facts about pit ponies

There were 66,000 ponies working underground in British pits in the year 1923. There were still 12,500 working below ground in 1955 in the N.C.B.'s time. This latter number was five years after Moston Colliery had been closed. Surprisingly, I never once saw a pony at work in the pit either above or below ground. The word "putter " was given to the man who spent his working day leading the ponies from coal seam to shaft and back to coal seam with the empties; these men and ponies had a special working relationship of trust and obedience to the man's voice.

In the Cumberland Coalfield, in order to keep the vermin down to a reasonable level in the pit, cats were taken down whilst still young and fussed and fed in the ponies' stable, so that this place became the centre of their lives. They ate rats or mice simply as a reward after the chase, but their main food was given to them by the men in and around the stable. These cats knew no other life but the one down below and appreciated their contact with the men who fed and cared for them, and had no reason except in fun to feed themselves. Living close to man became their way of life, so they stayed close to the area of the stables and its Ostler (see Figure 38). Unfortunately this situation was not repeated at Moston Pit in the 1920s (Howarth,1978).

It was a few years before my father came down to work in Manchester that Moston Pit's

Figure 38: An underground stable in a Cumberland pit. Notice the cats that live and are fed with the ponies, and are handled by the stableman Contrast this with the Moston Cat, which was shown no affection; it became wild in the workings, for if no bond exists between man and cat, then the cat has to kill to stay alive and would move away into the roadways to find food. (Photo reproduced with kind permission of Anne and Bill Thomas).

troubles started. The pit had an increasing problem with the rat population growing ever larger and often seen in the area of the stables. It can be understood with hindsight why the stable area was the source of most of the trouble, for the ponies were always fed and watered there. Because of the scarcity of food for the rats, anything dropped was an additional source to fight over, for privation increased the formation of a pecking order in the rat population and fights started up around the ponies' legs by the more dominant rats. A sense of timing formed, driven by the hour that the ponies were fed, and so the boss rats would always appear at the correct times, i.e. just after feeding, often after the Ostler had gone away. Rats, having a quarrelsome nature, tended to be noisy when asserting their rank, and so squealing and fights occurred often.

This behaviour began to affect the ponies as well, and the more nervous ones ate less food and could not relax after their shift had finished. When the Ostler noticed how nervous his charges were becoming, he decided to do something about it. He thought on this problem for some time and eventually decided the answer lay in the prowess of a hungry cat. He brought down to the stable area a half-grown male cat and the plan was not to feed it at all so that it would kill to live and eat rats day after day. In doing so perhaps the problem would resolve itself given some time and a hungry cat. The cat disappeared away into the darkness and was not seen for many days; not surprisingly it did not show any fondness for the man who had carried it down and never returned to him at the stables. The cat prospered, soon learning his feeding routine, and never seemed short of a meal. The area about the stables became less bothered with vermin and so the cat moved further away into the darkness to

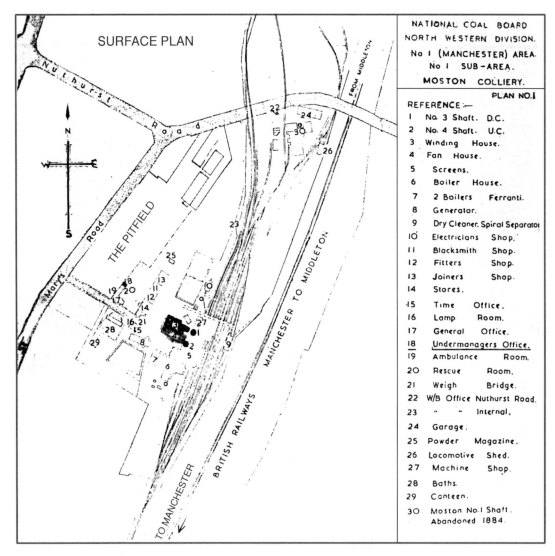

Figure 39: The layout of the pit top at Moston 3 and 4 shafts.

seek his food, catching and eating as he went. He was seen less often now, so it grew up wild in the workings and waste places of the pit and was not under the control of any human being.

Time passed and the pit worked on, but sad to say the men were beginning to be uneasy with the cat now, and it was becoming as big a problem as the rats had been some months earlier. As the numbers of rats reduced, so the cat became bolder and could often be heard scampering in the half light between groups of men, but so quickly that most often nothing was seen. As men passed up or down the roadways, a pair of green eyes was often seen from the darkness looking back at them, and because all was silent this unnerved some of the miners. Generally it gave no trouble to men in groups, but the luckless fireman who tested for gas before the men started their shift was forced by his job to start early, and always went alone. On some occasions he was set upon as he passed a low place and was not in a position to fend off an attack by the cat, though it might be said today that it only sought something to play with, as cats will do.

It was said around the pit that a deputy had been scratched and bitten as he walked alone to his next place of blasting, and these sudden attacks invariably came from behind, giving the lone recipient a nasty shock. A sudden attack gave a man no advantage at all, especially so because the light that was carried was so low in intensity. Mutterings of complaint went through the pit, for any miner working alone was a potential target for the cat. The complaints went unheeded until some member of the management team noticed that men never walked or worked alone, and indeed one became the defender of the other. In a situation like a working pit, this kind of action can't be tolerated, for the manager came to realise that the moving in pairs for mutual safety cost the management an extra wage for no extra work.

Now things started happening at the pit. The manager had poisons put down all along one wall of the main roadway, both to the west and east of the pit bottom. This did no good for the rats that were still living in the pit bottom were getting to the poison first, and the 'wild cat of Moston' still lived on. When it was realised that this ploy had not worked and the poison was not attracting the cat, the manager had a notice placed on the notice board near to the lamp room to this effect:

"The Management of this Colliery do offer the grand sum of Two Pounds Ten Shillings for the cat, dead or alive, this shall be paid next pay day, to the successful wage earner."

This was a good amount as far as rewards go at this time in the early 1920s, so plenty tried, but not one worker had any success in catching the cat. However, a pit deputy was in his local inn one night, when a professional rat catcher came in and by sheer luck sat next to the deputy. They were soon engaged in serious conversation together, and so the sad tale of the troublesome cat was related to the rat catcher. He smiled in sympathy and stated that if permission could be got off the manager to go down the pit with a guide, then he, the rat catcher, would do what was necessary.

With permission granted, one pit deputy slept better that night in his bed; any dreams that he dreamt were likely to have been of his reward and how he could spend it. On the following night as arranged, the two men met up near the General Office situated in the pit yard. The rat catcher had down his coat a she-cat that was very friendly and in season, and round its neck was a collar with a short lead fixed to it. He also carried a length of iron bar, but this was not at first noticed by the deputy. At shaft bottom they set off inbye, and as the air in a coal pit goes but one way round, it wouldn't have mattered just where the she-cat was, for a strong message would have rushed round the workings, broadcasting her amorous condition. It couldn't have been an easy matter to persuade the cat to walk along with the men on its lead, but the ordeal was soon over for suddenly a black furry monster had jumped upon the she-cats' back, its eyes blazing with lust, for it had waited a long time for this moment. There was a flash of moving iron and a dull thud, and the monster of Moston Pit gave trouble no more.

Things soon returned to normal at the pit; the men were able to walk alone once more through the places they knew and frequented. The debt was paid in full round the bar in the local inn, the rat catcher going away a very happy man that evening with an empty bottle in his hand. The pit deputy was paid his reward on his pay day and normality returned to a working pit.

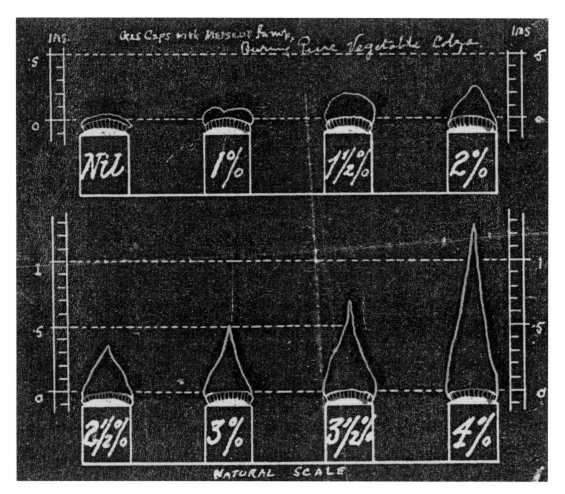

Figure 40: Testing For Gas. This diagram from my father's papers, illustrates how the flame in a safety lamp spires up as the percentage of firedamp in the workings increases. In a very high percentage of gas, the lamp would extinguish itself, the flame going out in the lamp. A very experienced man who tested for gas on a regular basis was said to be able to estimate the, percentage of gas just by looking at the height of the flame. To test for gas the flame would be turned down initially to its smallest. In a gassy atmosphere the flame colour changes as well as spiring up, i.e. becoming longer.

18
A VERY IMPORTANT MARINE BAND

In 1927 Professor George Hickling published a book giving sections of the strata passed through by many shafts in the county of Lancashire. For Moston No. 3 Pit he lists layer 74 down from the surface, as a hard gray rock, 1foot 6 inches thick, but the original shaft section from 1887 describes this a little differently as, "layer 74 (HARD GRAY WINN ROCK) 1 foot 6 inches thick". The word 'Winn' was left off by the professor and I wondered why. I couldn't quite remember what this word meant, so I looked it up and this was the answer: "*Winn, a very hard rock often of volcanic origin*". Now I understood: our professor knew this layer was not volcanic and omitted it from his book. The reason the word 'winn' was used is this. In 1887 when No. 3 shaft was being sunk, a geologist or the person who drew the maps for Moston Pit, was sent down each day, or at least once a week over the three years of sinking, to note down and measure each band of rock uncovered. His description of the bands of rock was all important for once the tubbing had been inserted no human eye would ever see that rock again. This person noticed that this one band was much harder rock than any other that had been cut through, and he described it as 'winn', a word from the northeast of Britain. He failed to realise that this hard band was in fact a marine band, wrapped up in a very hard limestone.

This unrecognised siting was of the famous Dukinfield Marine Band of Lancashire, that is now renamed *Aegiranum*, and contained shells that lived in the sea during the formation of our coal seams about 300 million years ago. The mechanism suggests a transgression of the sea onto the newly formed land surface in coal forming times. It was 25 years earlier that this marine band had first been found and studied and was unfortunately not spotted at Moston's No. 3 shaft sinking, nor at many other shafts of that period. In the science of geology at that time this marine band was of the greatest importance, but to a shaft-sinker in the dark of a wet dripping shaft, looking for shells was not on his list of priorities. Here follows the story of this important shell band and its first finding in Lancashire.

In 1862, Mr Edward Hull with his colleague Mr Green working for the Geological Survey, were making their way up the Coal Measures in east Lancashire and I quote:

> "I and my colleague, Mr Green, were perfectly astounded by a discovery we made a short time ago in the coal strata of this district. After tracing up the lower coals from the Gannister series [now called the Lower Mountain Mine coal] containing marine shells, at Stalybridge, along the river to the Dukinfield collieries, we seemed to be getting to the very upper part of the Coal Measures. We found on the bank of the river, near the canal and railway bridge, large nodular masses of semi-calcareous grit, embedded in shale, and cropping out in places. My friend and colleague, Mr Green, was a little ahead of me. I had clambered down to the bank, and was picking

at these nodules, when he called out, 'Here are goniatites' and there they were as large as life, with several shells, the *Aviculopectin papyraceus*, and others, which have always hitherto been considered to be confined to the lower Coal Measures, and to the series of strata below the Arley mine. We set to work on the spot, and got out some specimens, which have since been sent to Mr Salter, who says they are shells belonging to the same genera as those which are found in the lower Coal Measures" [of Westphalian A age. He went on to say that though these measures have never before been pierced about Ashton or Dukinfield, there can be no question that they belong to the upper part of the Coal Measures.] No doubt there is a little fault running at the back of these beds, but it would require a fault of perhaps 4,000 or 5,000 feet to bring up the Lower Coal Measures into that position, and there is no fault of anything like that extent in the neighbourhood. Therefore we felt perfectly sure that these shales and the embedded fossils belong to the top of the middle part of the coal series, lying, of course, below all the Ardwick Limestone series, and above all the thick coal-seams."

The Ardwick Limestone Series is in Westphalian D. The name Dukinfield Marine Band became the local name in Lancashire, and more recently the name of *Aegiranum* is recognised and understood throughout Britain's coalfields, for the *Aegiranum* shell is particular to this Marine Band. This was the first sighting in Lancashire of *Aegiranum*.

Time moved on, and at a meeting of the Manchester Geological Society in 1881, Mr George Wild said:

"that if this bed should prove to be unique, as I believe it is, so far as at present known, in the thick-series of the middle Coal Measures which exist on the western side of Ashton-under-Lyne, it cannot fail to have a highly practical diagnostic value to a Society which combines mining with structural and paleontological geology."

He went on to say:

"together with others, I long felt uncertain, in the absence of direct proof, as to whether the bed cropping out in the river Tame, containing Goniatites, Aviculo-pectens, Orthoceratites, &c, was occupying a true position in the measures, the section of which below this bed was thought to be well known."

He had many conversations with his friends on the subject, and a little over a year later they visited the Tame and made careful examination of the bed which is to be seen in the eastern bank of the river near Walk Mill:

"We obtained several fine specimens. We discussed the question as to continuity of the bed, the probable depth it should be met with in the AshtonMoss sinking. [The new first shaft for the Ashton Moss Colliery had been sunk and called No. 1 shaft.] Feeling anxious lest the bed should be sunk through unobserved, I paid frequent visits to the colliery with a view of making enquiries and examining the shale heaps, but I got no sign or tidings of it until October last, when I had the good fortune to find a shale which appears to correspond accurately with the bed outcropping in the Tame".

Mr Wild suggested that the shells seen from these two places must form a continuous horizon and so can form a datum line that should be watched for in further shaft sinkings in the future. At this point he made an estimate for the depth down to the three expected coals at Ashton Moss Colliery (the Sod Mine, the Ashton Great Mine and the Roger), based upon measurements made in the bed of the River Tame. He stated that, "the inclination of the strata to be about 35°, and direction W. S. W." [Because a large fault crossed the New Moss Shaft, the true depth of this marine band in the shaft was never known in Mr Wild's lifetime.] In the fullness of time his original calculations for the coals were proved correct. This was the 2nd sighting in Lancashire of *Aegiranum*.

Some patient watching and waiting by Mr Wild on the spoil heap of the New Moss Shaft finally gave proof and added to our understanding of the southeast Lancashire Coalfield, but why had this band never been seen before? It is a fact that many old shafts had already gone through this band including at least two at Moston, and possibly all five? I know that at Bradford Colliery, the Parker Shaft borehole and later the Deep Shaft, both rushed through it without any recognition that it contained shells when sunk in 1876 and 1904 respectively. All came right in the end, however, for in the late 1920s, during a re-survey by the men of the Geological Survey. This marine band was deliberately looked for and found in the return airway that ran from Deep Mine at Bradford Colliery, round the coal workings then back up to the base of the Parker Shaft, this shaft being the upcast shaft for the pit. Found at about 200 feet below the base of the Parker Shaft, it consisted of 1ft 3ins of hard limestone over 9 inches of fossiliferous shale. This was the 3rd sighting in Lancashire of *Aegiranum*.

The last siting was a wonderfull thing, for when seen it was realised that for the very first time the band had been found beyond the Great Irwell Valley Fault. Just south of Little Lever and next to Farnworth Cemetery, the Nob End Brickworks Quarry gave just a small glimpse of the marine band. Now it was known that its continuity was in place and the *Aegiranum* band of shells could, and probably does, cross the whole of the Lancashire Coalfield from Ashton-under-Lyne in the east to St Helens in the west. To quote from the men of the Ordnance Survey, these sitings:

"make the relationship established between the Bradford measures and the Oldham succession and the correlation of the eastern and western coalfields absolute" (Tonks *et al.*, 1931, p. 55). This was the 4th sighting in Lancashire of *Aegiranum*.

The approximate dates of sightings of this marine band, and missed sightings:

The very first sighting, Bank of the River Tame at Dukinfield – 1862

Sighting missed in the Parker Shaft at Bradford Colliery when a hole 471 feet deep was drilled at the then shaft bottom, but no shells spotted – 1876

Seen on the Pit Bank, New Moss Colliery by Mr George Wild – 1879

Sighting missed at Moston Colliery; 3-4 sinkings but although the thickness of the shells' host rock was measured accurately, shells not noted – 1885. Sighting missed at the Deep Shaft sinking, Bradford Colliery – 1904

Seen in the brick works quarry at Nob End, near to Farnworth Cemetary – 1928

Looked for and found in the return airway, 200 feet below the Parker Coal at Bradford Colliery – 1928

The shaft sinkers failed in many other shafts, to see the shells that mark the marine band, that is now called *Aegiranum*. The dates are approximate.

Aegiranum, is but one of many marine bands found interspersed between the seams of coal in Lancashire, but this one above all others became, when recognised at various pits, a sort of datum line which enabled many problems of correlation in the higher Coal Measures to be solved. These marine bands contain the remains of shelled creatures that lived in saltwater (i.e. in the sea).

There are other shelled creatures to be found interspersed between layers of rock, and the next section deals with these creatures that once lived exclusively in fresh water. These lived their lives in the mud or sand of the coal-forming deltas, the fresh water running down off a land surface bringing plant debris that later formed into coal. We call these shells *Carbonicola*, and these fossil shells represent the houses in which the creatures lived whilst alive, during coal forming times.

Figure 41: The fossil fresh water-shell, *Anthraconaia richfordi,* collected from Moston Colliery 140 feet below the Hathershaw Seam in the Chamber Rock. (See below for details of the naming of *Carbonicola* from Moston Pit.)

19
CARBONICOLA, A SCIENTIFIC STUDY

Carbonicola is a fossil shell, different in many respects to the types that are present in the marine bands, but unique in that they were alive during coal forming times and lived their lives in fresh water that was bordering on brackish.

In 1931 the results of a wonderful piece of research were first published by the H.M.S.O. This was the culmination of many years of study and hard work in the Lancashire Coalfield by some eminent people of the Geological Survey. In this study the findings and results of work done by the members of the Manchester Geological Society in former years was included and used as a starting point. Work done by great men of a former age was checked and incorporated in this new study. Moston Pit played an important role, for the Moston tunnels from Platt to Black Mine, as well as the Platt and the Hardman tunnels, were studied and examined, and the rock material from certain places was brought up to the surface to be seen in the light of day. Beds exposed in the tunnels were closely examined, their lithological characters noted, and fossiliferous horizons located. Through the courtesy of the officials at the pit, the actual collecting was done at the surface as tubs of material were brought up from each band. Fossils from at least twenty *Carbonicola* bands were seen, many being recorded for the very first time. This study was widened to other pits, Bradford Colliery being one of them.

The return airway from Deep Mine up to the base of the Parker Shaft, as mentioned earlier, was examined, and five fossil bands were found to contain the same shells as at Moston. These combined tunnel sections give a cross section of the Coal Measures for something like 1,800 feet; 480 feet of measures overlap and are present at both pits. A greater understanding of our coalfield came from this study, and it became possible, because of the identification of the shell bands, to recognise a coal seam, and also its twin in another district, simply by identifying the nearest shell band to the coal. Some seams were given different names in two areas, but now the mechanism was there to see if they were both the same coals and the uncertainties were somewhat lessened. It became apparent also that the lower good coals at Bradford Colliery were the same seams as the higher good coals at Moston. This meant that Bradford which is in the central Manchester coalfield, and never knew its place in the overall picture, could now sit as an equal with Oldham and Ashton in the southeast Lancashire coalfield. If I understand correctly, as a form of gratitude for the help of the Moston management as stated above, a new species of shell was given the name of the General Manager, Mr Herbert Richford. So an important little shell from Moston Colliery was given the name *Anthraconaia richfordi* after the manager at that time (Tonks *et al.* 1931).

It was a long time ago that the pit at Moston was sinking new shafts, Nos 3 and 4 being completed in 1887. In the early days there was no understanding at all of these random shells occurring at uneven intervals in the Coal Measures and between the coal seams. A lot depended upon which team was doing the sinking, and how observant they were. Even the words used to describe a rock would vary from team to team; a sort of dialect, or preference of words used, moved around from site to site with each team of shaft sinkers. At Moston in 1887 only three shell bands were entered on the detailed list of the shaft section, and at Bradford Colliery with the deep shaft sinking in 1904, five shell bands were noted.

I have already told the story of the British Geological Survey people painstakingly examining every yard of the passageways below the Parker Shaft at Bradford, and the same care was exercised at Moston from the Black Mine upwards for many hundreds of feet. Sixteen separate layers of shells were discovered in the tunnels at Moston, many seen for the very first time in this coalfield, and eight layers were found at Bradford. The most important thing was that five bands were found in a similar position at both pits and this was called the overlap. The paucity of detail along with the complication of the Moston Fault makes it difficult to set out a table of shell sitings, and to supply an accurate depth for each band.

A list of shell bands found in the Moston tunnels in the late 1920s and their approximate depth down below the surface as they crossed No. 3 shaft is given below:

The *Aegiranum* band of marine shells; limestone noted, but shells not seen – 354 feet.
Carbonicola band – 220 feet above Major Seam at 858 feet.
Carbonicola band – 160 feet above Major Seam at 918 feet.
Carbonicola band – 100 feet above Major Seam at 978 feet.
Major Mine (the coal seam) – 1,088 feet.
Carbonicola band – 11 feet below Major Seam at 1,099 feet.
Carbonicola band – 90 feet below Major Seam at 1,178 feet.
Roger Mine (the coal seam) – 1,298 feet.
Carbonicola band – 35 feet below Roger Seam at 1,333 feet.
Carbonicola band – 52 feet below Roger Seam at 1,354 feet.
Carbonicola band – above the roof of Stubbs Mine Seam at 1,532 feet?
Carbonicola band – 65 feet below Mary Seam.
Carbonicola band – 535 feet above the Platt Seam.
Carbonicola band – 510 feet above Platt Seam.
Carbonicola band – 480 feet above Platt Seam.
Carbonicola band – 440 feet above Platt Seam.
Carbonicola band – 320 feet above Platt Seam.
Carbonicola band – 280 feet above Platt Seam.
Carbonicola band – a few feet above the Platt Seam at approximately 1,800 feet.

Figure 42 (opposite): Some statistics from No. 3 shaft in 1887. Layer 74 marks the position of the Dukinfield Marine Band in No. 3 shaft at Moston. Shells not noticed at sinking. This marine band is now renamed the *Aegiranum* band.

90—MOSTON COLLIERY, No. 3 PIT.

Sheet XCVI. S.E.

N. 53° 30′ 54″.   W. 2° 10′ 30″.   885020

	FT. IN.	FT. IN.
1 Soil	1 0	
2 Clay	36 0	
3 Sand and gravel	0 10	
4 Dry sand	6 9	
5 Fine loamy sand	15 0	
6 Soft clay	0 10	
7 Quick sand	1 2	
8 Brown clay	1 0	
9 Quick sand	1 7	
10 Strong brown boulder clay	38 0	
11 Quick sand	1 4	
12 Strong boulder clay	40 0	
13 Clay containing a quantity of large and small boulder stones	6 0	
14 Fine loamy sand	1 0	
15 Sand and gravel with large boulders	20 4	
16 Red and grey shales	7 6	
17 Soft red sandstones	0 10	
18 Red and grey sandy shales	21 0	
19 Dark grey shales	6 0	
20 Grey sandstone	1 0	
21 Soft grey sandstone	0 6	
22 Blue shale	2 0	
23 Grey rock	6 0	
24 Grey shale	1 6	
25 Black shale	3 0	
26 Grey shale	2 6	
27 Dark blue shale		
28 Grey shale with ironstone bands	6 0	
29 Black shale	1 6	
30 COAL	1 2	
Grey shale with bands of ironstone	2 0	
R COAL	2 8	
Fireclay	0 7	
COAL	1 7	240 2
31 Strong fireclay	4 7	
32 Grey sandstone	0 6	
33 Blue shale	3 0	
34 Black shale	0 4	
35 COAL	1 0	249 7
36 Grey sandy shale	3 0	
37 Grey sandy shale with coal joints	12 0	
38 Cank with spar joints	1 1	
39 Blue shale	3 4	
40 COAL	1 0	270 0
41 Fireclay	1 1	
42 Ironstone	0 1½	
43 Grey sandstone	2 3	
44 Dark grey sandy shale with layers of grey sandstone and black joints	1 6	
45 Light reddish grey sandstone	1 8	
46 Stoney dark grey sandy shale	5 6	
47 Red and grey sandstone	1 2	
48 Grey sandstone	2 10	
49 Blue shale with layers of sandstone	5 8	
50 Ironstone band	0 1	
51 Black shale and Bassy COAL	1 4	293 2½
52 Strong fireclay with COAL joints	2 6½	
53 Dark grey sandy shale	5 8	
54 Grey sandstone	1 0	
55 Sandstone with streaky appearance	0 4	
56 Grey sandstone	2 3	
57 Sandstone and COAL joints	4 2	
58 Hard grey sandstone	4 0	
59 Hard grey sandstone	0 4	
60 Soft grey sandstone	0 10	
61 Bluish grey shale	6 9	
62 Black shale	1 11	
63 Light bluish grey shale	1 9	
64 Dark grey shale	1 0	
65 COAL	0 7	
Fireclay and balls of ironstone	3 9	
Dark grey shale	0 4	
COAL	0 8	331 1

	FT. IN.	FT. IN.
66 Dark shale	1 9	
67 Bands of ironstone with spar joints	0 4	
68 Strong fireclay	2 6	
69 Grey sandstone with joints	3 7	
70 Grey sandy shale	3 3	
71 Sandstone	0 8	
72 Sandstone with grey shale partings	1 7	
73 Blue shale	8 6	
74 Hard grey rock	1 6	←
75 Dark grey sandy shale	26 7	
76 Dark blue shale with layers of ironstone	3 0	
77 COAL	1 6	385 10
78 Bat	0 3	
79 Fireclay with COAL joints	4 0	
80 Balls of sandstone	3 6	
81 Grey sandy shale	3 7	
82 Grey shale	12 10	
83 COAL	1 7	411 7
84 Fireclay with balls of ironstone	7 1	
85 Fireclay, strong	7 0	
86 Grey shale	13 0	
87 Grey sandstone	1 0	
88 Grey sandy shale	5 9	
89 Soft grey sandstone	2 3	
90 Grey rock with spar joints	8 9	
91 Grey shale	8 4	
92 Soft sandstone	2 0	
93 Grey sandy shale	22 0	
94 Clunch	2 6	
95 Strong dark grey sandy shale	45 0	
96 Grey shale with bands of ironstone	51 10	
97 Clunch parting		
98 Blue shale with balls of ironstone	7 6	
99 COAL	1 3	597 1
100 Grey loamy shale	11 6	
101 Clunch	1 0	
102 Black shale with COAL joints	0 6	
103 Grey sandstone	3 5	
104 COAL	1 10	615 4
105 Under clay	0 7	
106 Strong fireclay	0 8	
107 Fireclay	3 0	
108 Strong rock	1 9	
109 Fireclay with ironstone balls	4 3	
110 Strong grey rock	1 0	
111 Shale with joints	6 0	
112 COAL	1 0	634 7
113 Alum shale	0 8	
114 Alum shale	1 4	
115 Shale	3 2	
116 Strong grey rock	1 6	
117 Strong shale with streaks of iron	3 2	
118 Strong grey shale	1 6	
119 Strong shale with iron bands	0 6	
120 Shaley bind or soapstone	4 6	
121 COAL	1 5	652 4
122 Shale with dark partings	8 5	
123 Sandy grey rock	6 8	
124 Strong shaley bind	10 9	
125 Strong bind	9 0	
126 Soft alum shale	1 1	
127 Bastard COAL, faulty	1 0	689 3
128 Fireclay	2 2	

	FT. IN.	FT. IN.
129 Strong blue shaley bind with cross joints	17 8	
130 Grey sandstone with black partings	8 10	
131 Strong rock band	1 0	
132 Blue shaley bind	18 10	
133 Soft fireclay or clunch	0 6	
134 Strong grey shale with dark partings	13 2	
135 Strong grey shale	13 8	
136 Grey sandstone rock	4 0	
137 Blue shaley bind	20 9	
138 Ironstone band	0 4	
139 Dark shale	0 6	
140 Ironstone band	0 2	
141 Soft shaley bind	0 10	
142 Clear COAL, fairly good	2 4	
Bastard COAL or bottoms	0 4	794 4
143 Under clay or holing dirt	0 1	
144 Strong fireclay floor	17 0	
145 Blue shaley bind	25 0	
146 Strong fireclay	5 0	
147 Blue shaley bind	6 0	
148 Soft dark shale	0 10	
149 Strong iron band	0 6	
150 COAL	1 0	
Dark parting fireclay	1 7	
Bastard Cannel COAL	0 10	
Strong fireclay	0 11	
Cannel COAL	0 2	853 3
151 Strong cank band	0 8	
152 Shaley bind	12 0	
153 Strong grey sandstone	15 9	
154 Shaley bind	8 3	
155 COAL	0 11	890 10
156 Soft fireclay	1 3	
157 Strong fireclay	3 0	
158 Very hard sandstone rock	6 0	
159 Dark shaley bind	9 10	
160 Black Cannel COAL	4 0	920 11
161 Fireclay	1 3	
162 Shale with ironstone	27 3	
163 Strong iron band	0 6	
164 Blue shale with iron bands	12 0	
165 COAL, very good quality	2 5	964 4
166 Dark shale and COAL	0 6	
167 Soft holing dirt	0 5	
168 Blue shaley bind with iron band	19 6	
169 COAL	2 5	
Dark shale or holing dirt	0 11	
P COAL	0 8	988 9
170 Strong grey sandstone	6 0	
171 Grey sandstone rock	7 0	
172 Grey sandstone with ironstones	5 0	
173 Ironstone band	0 4	
174 Strong grey shale	7 0	
175 Ironstone band	0 6	
176 Strong shale with bands of stone	8 10	
177 COAL	1 7	1025 0
178 Soft shale	0 8	
179 Grey sandstone	4 0	
180 Soft dark coaly shale	2 3	
181 Shale with ironstone bands	22 0	
182 COAL	1 1	1055 0
183 Fireclay	2 5	
184 Strong sandstone shale	9 6	
185 Blue sandy shale	14 2	
186 Blue sandy bind	3 0	
187 Major Mine—		
COAL	1 10	
O Holing dirt	0 6	
COAL	1 8	1088 1
188 Soft fireclay	1 0	
189 Blue shaley bind	3 0	
190 Strong shale with ironstone balls	6 0	
191 Shell band with dark shale	1 1	
192 Blue shaley bind	1 0	
193 Strong grey sandstone rock	4 0	

Figure 42 (continuation)

SECTIONS OF STRATA OF THE

90—MOSTON COLLIERY, No. 3 PIT.—*Continued.*

	FT.	IN.	FT.	IN.
194 Soft dark shale parting	0	1		
195 Strong ironstone band	0	4		
196 Soft dark shale parting	0	1		
197 Very strong sandstone rock	5	4		
198 Strong grey sandstone shale	7	0		
199 Strong grey shale with ironstone bands	11	10		
200 Ironstone band	0	2		
201 Blue shaley bind	10	0		
202 Black shale	3	9		
203 Blue shaley bind	0	8		
204 Dark soft clay parting	0	3		
205 Blue shaley bind	1	6		
206 Ironstone band	0	1		
207 Dark soft loamy parting	0	3		
208 Dark shale with ironstone band	1	2		
209 COAL	0	11		
Grey shale with ironstone bands	2	11		

	FT.	IN.	FT.	IN.
COAL	1	6		
			1152	0
210 Strong dark grey shale with ironstone bands	23	0		
211 COAL	0	5½		
			1175	5½
212 Dark shale with ironstone bands	14	4		
213 Dark shale with ironstone bands	14	8		
214 Grey shale	1	0		
215 Dark soft shaley parting	0	4		
216 Dark blue shale	4	6		
217 Colonel Mine—				
M COAL	3	8		
			1213	11½
218 Strong fireclay	4	0		
219 Dark soft shaley parting	0	2½		
220 Strong fireclay	2	0		
221 Strong grey sandstone shale	24	2		
222 Grey cank rock	4	10		
223 Strong grey sandstone shale	10	0		
224 Strong grey sandstone shale	29	9		
225 Soft blue shale or following dirt	2	0		
226 Big Mine—				
COAL tops	6	3		
Dirt	0	5		
L COAL bottoms	0	9½		
			1298	4½
227 Alum shale	3	6½		
228 Blue shaley bind	11	0		
229 Ironstone band	0	4		
230 Grey sandstone rock	3	11		
231 Strong sandstone shale	7	6		
232 Strong blue shale with ironstone	8	0		
233 Shell bed	0	7		
234 Blue shaley bed	4	0		
235 Ironstone band	0	4		
236 Dark blue shale	2	5		
237 Soft shaley parting	0	3		
238 Grey shale	1	11		
239 Ironstone band	0	3		
240 Grey shale with ironstone balls	10	10		
241 Shell bed	1	0		
242 Strong grey shale with ironstone band	23	11		
243 Blue shaley bind	5	4		
244 Soft clunch parting	0	4		
245 Black ironstone band	0	4		
246 Devil Mine—				
COAL	2	6		
			1386	8

	FT.	IN.	FT.	IN.
247 Dark soft shale	1	4		
248 Light grey shale	3	6		
249 Soft blue shale	6	6		
250 Soft blue shale	1	4		
251 Foxholes Mine—				
Top COAL	2	3		
Dirt	0	3		
Bottom COAL	1	4		
Holing dirt	0	5		
COAL parting	0	2		
			1403	9
252 Soft fireclay	0	4		
253 Strong fireclay	2	8		
254 Blue shale with bright parting	5	3		
255 Grey sandstone shale	6	0		
256 Grey sandstone shale	21	2		
257 Bands of ironstone and sandstone shale with dark partings	21	0		
258 Dark shale	1	0		
259 Light sandstone rock	1	3		
260 Grey sandstone rock with dark partings	6	9		
261 Grey sandstone rock, cross joints and much broken by faults	9	2		
262 Grey and red sandstone rock with pockets of red ochre	43	3		

	FT.	IN.	FT.	IN.
263 COAL parting	0	2½		
			1532	9¼

From this point for about 84 yards it is all faulty ground with no regular measures.

	FT.	IN.	FT.	IN.
264 Soft slatey greasy shale and mottled conglomerate rock	5	10		
265 Very soft faulty ground, containing a mixture of COAL, rock and various other substances	6	0		
266 Faulty ground, containing no regular measures, some large rocks at various angles intermixed with many different metals, etc.	240	2		
267 Grey sandstone shale	1	1		
268 Grey sandy shale with dark streaks and well marked	18	0		
			1803	10¼

<-- ----- Layer 74 on previous page marks the position of the Dukinfield Marine Band in No 3 shaft at Moston. Shells not noticed at sinking

This Marine Band is now re-named the *Ægiranum*

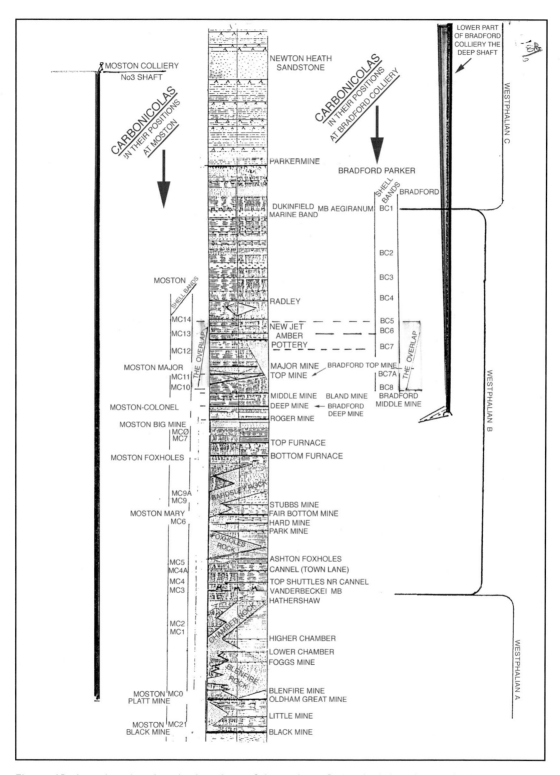

Figure 43: A section showing the locations of the various *Carbonicola* bands seen in the deep workings at Moston and Bradford in the late 1920s (note the overlap, same shells at both pits).

The following is a short glossary of words used in the Moston Colliery No. 3 shaft section with their meanings. Nowadays we no longer understand these nearly forgotten words and in truth these words were always of a rather specialised nature, confined to pits and to shaft sinking, and not words of general knowledge even in days gone by:

Bass:	Black carbonaceous shale, a stony coal.
Bind:	A parting, usually of shale or mudstone.
Bone Coal:	A hard cannaloid coal of lighter weight.
Brassy coal:	Coal that has a proportion of iron pyrites.
Cank:	A compact sandstone with high iron content.
Cannel Coal:	A light weight coal of fine grain with no visible plant material.
Clunch:	Unlaminated clay or shale, forms dirt partings in coal seams.
Dirt Parting:	A band of rock or shale dividing a coal seam into two or more parts.
Fireclay:	Fine grained compact sandstone, often showing roots of Coal Measure plants.
Gannister:	Fine compact sandstone, with a high silica content usually unbedded.
Holing Dirt:	An inferior band of coal that can be removed by pick or machine to undercut the coal seam.
Ironstone:	An iron impregnated sandstone in layers, sometimes of nodular appearance.
Metal:	The old fashioned way of describing shale rock in a pit.
Mussel Band:	Usually a band of shale complete with fossil shells *in situ*.
Raddle:	An ironstone band.
Rag:	A layer of flagstone, suitable for flagstone paths etc.
Seat Earth:	As in fireclay, the present rock floor in which coal plants had their roots (also called the seat or the seating).
Shaley Bind:	A shale or mudstone layer that breaks off in layers.
Smut:	Soft powdery or friable coal or carbonaceous shale.
Soapstone:	A fine unlaminated shale, smooth to the touch, slippery to walk on.

20
A MOSTON MISCELLANY

Accidents in the Pit

In the early days of coal mines with shafts, the incidents and accidents in the mines were at a very high level, many accidents causing death and disablement to the miners. As the years went by, statistics began to be kept, and as a result a start was made to understanding why and how these accidents had happened. Many of the safety features that came later had not been thought of in those earlier times when steam power was just coming into use, and simple cages were taking over from the corves of older times. An example of this lack of foresight are the early cages held in position by only two wires called conductors which stopped the cage from swinging about in the shaft. Although descending at a speed of perhaps 30 mph, no safety gates were fitted to the cage sides, so that any unevenness in the travel could throw the men out to their deaths below. Worse, the early cages had no roof protection fitted at all, so that the cage was just open to the sky. Many men were killed by objects falling out of the shaft side or dropping from the surface above.

The smaller pits never made the effort to become safety conscious for often the management did not want to spend money on safety, and at that time life was cheap. As time passed and coal pits became deeper, laws were eventually passed and Acts of Parliament put pressure on the mines to improve things, but pressure had to be exerted to cut down the appalling numbers dying whilst getting coal to fuel the Industrial Revolution. By 1860 things were getting better, but even at the turn of the century fatalities still occurred although fewer in number. As well as the pits' improvement, the world up top slowly improved as well. Hospitals were now available with early forms of ambulance. First aid was beginning to be taught and the best collieries had set up first aid rooms below ground. By 1940 Moston Colliery had 17 Ambulance stations in various districts below ground with trained staff to give aid when requested. Cloth caps were all that were worn to protect the head; late again, it was the 1940s before proper pit safety helmets were first used, initially made from compressed paper, lacquered to keep water from reshaping them when they got wet.

I wish I could report that this pit never had any accidents, but of course it has had its share, probably close to the national average. I will, however, list some instances that I came to hear about, just to set the record straight, for an accident on the surface is bad enough but any taking place hundreds of feet below the earth and as much as five miles from the shaft bottom is far more worrying to those concerned. Perhaps the very best thing that can be said is that at Moston Pit there is no record of a gas explosion. The pit did, however, have its share of outbursts of gas that were detected and dealt with, always successfully.

If we look back at the statistics of accidents in our pits, explosions of gas must rank as the worst and most horrid to the general public, for each blast killed large numbers of men in just a single incident. In any pit throughout its working life good practices like regular testing for gas saved many pits from having a potential explosion. At a later time when good mechanical ventilation came to pass, pits became much safer, for the gas was whisked away, and the percentage in the pit became lower, simply because the increased draught from the fan did not allow gas to linger in the roadways as much as before. It has been said that the management in early times did not value the lives of its workers, but on the other hand the men persisted in many areas, with unsafe practices like testing for gas with the open flame of a candle, even after the introduction of the safety lamp. When gas was detected and the flame of the candle lengthened (called spiring up), the other hand of the operator came carefully up beyond the flame in an act of cutting the flame off from the gas, a very risky move. This practice was banned in about 1851 bringing the end to a very dangerous way of testing for gas, and only then did the safety lamp come into general use.

Figure 44: "THE PENITENT" dressed for his safety in thick layers of wet sacking. Original drawing from *La Vie Souterraine* (Simonin, 1869).

Figure 44 shows a drawing of one of the earlier forms of Fireman who tested for gas in the hours before the men came on duty, and it was hoped he had cleared the pit of gas for at least some hours. This illustration came from France, but the method was also used here in Britain as well. Because of his posture he came to be called 'the Penitent', shown in a kneeling position, head facing the floor as if in supplication, and bravely, or foolishly depending on how you see it, he is holding a lighted glowing taper up into a gas pocket near the roof. The gas in this pocket would have exploded and in burning, this old pit was just that little bit safer thanks to this man doing a very dangerous job.

This fireman 'the Penitent' was dressed in thick wet sacking with a padded hood to protect his head. His taper was fixed onto a long stick, but this must have been the most dangerous job in the pit. With the wet sacking fixed over his head and down his back, he hoped never to get burned at least as long as the sacking stayed wet. This method was used in the years before 1700; his wages would be higher, but death would stalk through the roadways with him as he worked on all alone. Mostyn Colliery in North Wales was said to have had a 'penitent' as early as 1677. The smoke and gasses would have moved away very slowly, for air flow at that time was induced only by natural processes like temperature and atmospheric pressure, with a single shaft acting like a inefficient chimney. Moston's earlier shafts were not early enough to require a 'Penitent', and by 1840 No. 1 shaft had fitted state-of-the-art ventilation equipment making it for that time, a very modern Lancashire pit. It is beyond the scope of this book to go into great detail, but increased ventilation had to be matched in the roadways below with increasing vigilance. The introduction of an insufficient quantity of atmospheric air into a fiery mine may cause the very result against which increased ventilation was to guard. The pits at Moston worked high coal seams in what is termed The Middle Coal Measures, whereas in Oldham the productive coals were much lower in the system and these were far more gassy. The gas pressure in the coalface at the Nook Pit between Ashton and Oldham was so great, that many times it blew down the coal with a pressure comparable to it being blasted down, and was so powerful that the coal came down as a dust with particles of soft coal, which was unsaleable. Worst still, this condition took a number of lives and for many months the coal face had to be longlined or deep drilled in the hope that this would release some of the gas pressure. This was in the Arley Seam workings, the lowest workable coal in the Middle Coal Measures of Lancashire. At Oldham this coal was always called the Royley Seam. The biggest gas explosion in this district was at the early pit called Bardsley Colliery in 1858 when 53 men were killed, 46 of whom had serious burns. In his report the Inspector of Mines stated:

"the cause was evidently insufficient ventilation, owing to the airways being too small." [Some blame fell on the management for not heeding earlier warnings.]

This explosion occurred simultaneously in two separate coal seams, viz, the Two Feet Coal and the Peacock Coal. These two names were in regular use about Ashton and Dukinfield whereas the same seams in Oldham used the names of Upper and Lower Bent Mines; these coals were rated as gassy coals in most areas. The blast had been very intense, and in the levels near to the upcast shaft, timbers, trucks and wood fittings were all set on fire, and had to be quickly extinguished by those that had survived the blast. At Bardsley, the upcast shaft was called Victoria and the downcast shaft was called the Diamond Shaft.

The safety lamp became available for use years before the explosion at Bardsley Colliery though some of the early models themselves could become the cause of an explosion under certain circumstances. True safety did not come early or easily to the pits. Dr Clanny, a Medical Doctor from a coal mining district near to Sunderland, became concerned at the great loss of life due to gas explosions in his district. In 1813 he contributed a paper to the Royal Society on his newly invented safety lamp. This was the very first attempt to make a safety lamp that might show the presence of gas in the roadways below, but not in itself cause ignition. Other makers followed, but for many years safety could not be guaranteed in all conditions by any of the early lamps. Sir Humphrey Davy established a reputation for his lamp, and George Stevenson made great progress with his. Still many collieries refused to use safety lamps simply because in doing so it was thought to bring a bad name upon the colliery, and in truth, the safety lamp gave only a poor light, many times less than the candle flame.

During these early years only the pit fireman carried a safety lamp, and the miners themselves still used candles to work with, for these the men trusted. Even in 1835 mixed lighting was still in use, for it was nearly impossible to see with a safety lamp alone. Slowly improvements came along and by 1913 there were 740,000 flame safety lamps in use in this country which were used with more confidence in testing for gas. The gas comes mostly out of the coal itself as well as near to the roof and the floor and can be at a high pressure. After the explosion, those miners that survived the blast would quickly fall unconscious from the effects of the after damp, this containing carbon monoxide, a gas poisonous to man. Fine particles of coal dust, lifted up off the roadways by the flame, coated the wooden pit props with burning dust which turned to coke due to the lack of oxygen in those roadways. It took many years of research before this means of spreading the fire was properly understood. One warning of gas believed by the miners in early times, was an unexplained absence of rats or mice, or an uncharacteristic uneasiness in the pit ponies, who would kick at the floor if made to stand still in one place for too long.

The two instances of explosions of gas described above occurred at pits near to Ashton and Oldham. Despite their being no gas explosion at Moston, there would be many other ways that the miners of Moston pit came to their deaths, or were maimed or badly injured, and here are just a few examples to show the true realities of a working environment below the earth. Purely by chance I came across details of an accident in the shaft of the old pit (No.1 shaft), dating from August 27th 1858, and it just makes it plain that Moston Colliery was dirty, dark and a dangerous place for men to work in. Victims of accidents were taken up to the surface, but only if coal was not being wound at that time, the alternative being a long wait below for the injured man. A report by H. M. Inspectors of Mines, Mr Joseph Dickinson for 1858 states:

"In the shaft accident at the Moston Colliery on the 27th of August, the engine-man started the cage and crushed a person getting out of it, before the usual signal to go on was given by the hooker-on [later known as the 'Onsetter'], for which a verdict of manslaughter was returned against Thomas Hitchen the engine-man."

The trial took place at the Liverpool Winter Assizes, on Thursday December 16th and is reported as follows:

"Upon the examination of one witness, and the prisoner's statement before the Coroner being read, which fully showed that the death ensued from the prisoner's neglect to wait for the usual signal to start the engine, and that his excuse was, that it had escaped his memory that the deceased and others were in the cage which he had lowered down the pit; Mr Justice Hill at once directed the jury to acquit the prisoner, on the ground that there was not sufficient in the evidence to show that there was such negligence as amounted to manslaughter; that if he were guilty of manslaughter, a day's imprisonment would be sufficient punishment. After the verdict was recorded, his Lordship addressed the prisoner to the effect that it should be a warning to him to be more careful in future."

Mr G B Harrison, in his Presidential Address to the Manchester Geological and Mining Society in 1911 gave these frightening figures about pit accidents in the years 1873 to 1910 nationally. In those 37 years:

"6,305 men and boys died because of pit explosions.
18,161 men and boys died due to falls of ground or roof.
3,605 men and boys died in accidents in pit shafts.
9,595 men and boys died from other types of pit accidents."

A total of 37,666 in all. It is in fact well known that the further we go back in time, the more accidents occurred in each year, and conversely the nearer to our time we come, so the accident rate gets less.

Many smaller, less severe, accidents would consist of things like a fall of stone causing a mild concussion, the miner being taken to Ancoats Hospital and discharged later in the day. Or a few feet of coal face falling, and injuring a miner's foot, not broken, but badly bruised. Or length of shale roof falling in the Black Seam at Moston Colliery, trapping three men beyond the fall, rescued by colleagues after about 3 hours. The newspapers were not really interested in these small, less serious accidents, for in truth they happened on a daily basis and were not newsworthy. However, during my lifetime there was one very serious accident, one that most certainly brought the press into the area of the pit yard, notebooks in hand, and ready for any information. Mr H Richford, the General Manager, said later in the day:

> "The Company - Platt Bros & Co (Holdings) - regrets that an accident occurred at Moston Colliery at approximately 6.45 am during the process of lowering men down the incline of one in three, known as No. 17 slant. The grip [a special train designed for riding men underground], for some presently unknown reason got out of control. The Inspector of Mines, Mr D Coatsworth, and the representative of the workmen, Mr T Brown, are at the colliery investigating the cause of the accident."

Seven trucks were taking the men down to their work in the Roger Seam workings when it became derailed. Five men were killed and many men hurt in the accident. My father was in his fourteenth year at the pit and the war was in its second year.

On March 11th 1940 things went wrong in the dark levels of the pit. As each coal seam was followed away, in the general direction of Ashton-under-Lyne, every so often each seam along with the rock bands surrounding it, took a steep plunge downwards. Whether this plunge was fault induced, or just part of the crumpling of the measures during the Pennine uplift, is unclear, but it was indeed an awfully steep place, too steep for men to want to walk up after their working shift was over. This phenomenon gave rise to the need for a number of slants being required at the pit. So that the men understood where one slant was in relation to another, they had been given numbers like Slant 17, Slant 15, and Slant 10. From an early date these slants had been fitted up with a form of man rider, and in 1940 they were looking decidedly old-fashioned by later standards; as we would say now, "a little long in the tooth" (Harrison, 1911).

Nevertheless these early, if crude, man riders at this pit (called 'The Grip') were a real Godsend for a tired miner who had finished his shift somewhere under Daisy Nook and now on tired legs walking back outbye, suddenly saw an underground mountain rearing up before him (Slant 17). Crude and old-fashioned they may have been, but 'the grip' would have felt like an old armchair at that tired point in his working day. The slant gained height at something like 1 in 3, and was 900 feet long. I clearly remember in 1947 travelling in the grip myself down this very slant, though the accident was never mentioned to me at that time. I remember the trucks as being longer than a mine truck and I suspect they were made by the joiners at the pit, easy to walk into, but not very comfortable to sit in. Five or six persons were able to get in each man-riding truck and seven of these cars were linked to make a train that carried perhaps 40 men in total.

Each train of seven was pulled or let down by being fixed to a steel cable, and this cable had a quick release clip for its attachment, the cable being wound by a small engine that sat at the top of the slant in a small side extension. I am not certain whether a double set of rails descended down the slope. I can say, however, that in father's undated Photo (Fig. 46), two reels of haulage wire stand side-by-side in the winder, which suggests a pair of man-riders, one train lowering as the other came up the slope and passing at the halfway point of the slant. In essence the engine provided power to bring up from below one train full of men or coal. The empty train or a train taking men down the slope did not require any engine

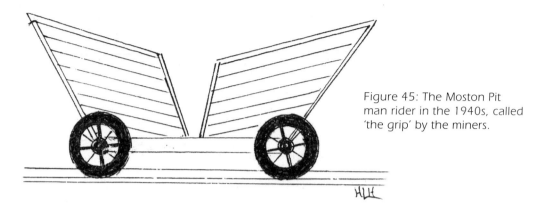

Figure 45: The Moston Pit man rider in the 1940s, called 'the grip' by the miners.

because gravity would take it down. However, in the latter case the engine would act to some extent as a brake to slow its speed of descent, making the braking only necessary when the gradient levels out at the bottom of the slant. There was, however, an unwritten rule that said when men are riding in the man-rider, the drive from the engine should always be in gear, i.e. the manual clutch is never pulled, thus using the drag from the engine as an additional brake. On March 11th 1940 it seems this rule was broken.

Years later I overheard the story of the accident. My father had been feeling the effects of sciatica and on the morning of the accident he was unable to get out of bed because of the pain. Later in the day the doctor was called and he was ordered to stay in the bed that he was unable to get out of at 3 am in the morning for his early shift. I suspect he felt sadness over the accident, for I heard him say years later, that had he been there at work that morning, the accident would not have happened. It was his place, when the regular slant driver stayed off work, to select a capable reserve driver for that day, and of course neither my father nor the regular driver had been at work on the day of the accident.

Slant 17 was below the bottom of Broadway near to its junction with Oldham Road and its depth at this point would be about 2,000 feet below the surface. This slant was the main way down to the workings on the Roger Seam, described as "Moston best coal". The colliers called it 'Big Mine' for this coal seam was 6ft 3ins thick with only one dirt parting in it.

This terrible accident caused the death of five miners; nine men with bad injuries were taken away to local hospitals and six others were treated on the spot, then helped out of the pit by the ambulance men who were already down below. The other nineteen poor miners hobbled back to the light like a wounded army returning from a battle, some with minor injuries, but mostly suffering from shock and disbelief. Only two miners escaped uninjured and they, sensing the acceleration coming at the place where it should be slowing down, jumped off the grip in a cloud of dust and so survived while the accelerating train crashed. The next length of haulage road below where the crash happened was where my uncle, George Tindall, worked. He was the maintenance man for that next stretch of passage. Being so near and hearing the terrible bang, he would have been early on the scene to help, but he never talked about what he saw. The shock of what he witnessed was so great that he went home that day and never set foot in a coal pit again. All of his life he had worked in the pits, and my father had actually encouraged him to come to Manchester when his former pit in Cumberland closed down.

As stated earlier one of the Inspectors of Mines, Mr D Coatsworth, arrived at the pit and immediately descended to the scene of the accident along with a representative of the workers, Mr T Brown, for it was essential that the cause of this accident was understood. It was soon noticed that the brake band, which applied the pressure to slow the haulage engine, had burst and this had allowed the grip to accelerate when it should have been slowing. The brake band was a strip of soft iron that held, via brass rivets, the lining of the brake. The iron was not thick and it was bent to form the same diameter as the lining material; the band was then connected via a link to the brake handle, which can be seen in Figure 46. Because the brake band was fixed firm at one end and to a moveable handle at the other end, variable braking could just about be achieved under normal operating conditions.

It must be apparent that in describing the accident at Slant 17, no mention has been made of the engine which brought up the coal from below the slant. My father's photograph (Figure 46) does not show an engine and I thought about this for many weeks without coming to any conclusion. I did not remember any noise or smell from when I travelled on the grip, but that was over fifty years ago. I thought about an internal combustion engine fitted with a scrubber to absorb any dangerous gasses and smells, but felt this would not be used in a working pit with explosive gas and a spark-creating engine. I next wondered if the engine and working parts had been taken above ground after the accident due to its being the cause, but this can't be so for both drums are shown on the photograph still *in situ* at the top of the slant. It must have been recognised early on that it was the brake mechanism which had failed.

Eventually light began to dawn. The development of the compressed air engine and its use in the coal pits was a rather slow process. Its first use was in about 1850, but it was not generally accepted as a form of power until after 1880, and by this date another source was coming along, namely electricity. Now, I believe that one of these two sources was used to power Slant 17 at Moston Pit, but I can't say which. The air compressor stood in the engine house for No. 3 pit; I saw it there myself and father photographed one in 1929 (Figure 33). The high pressure air was piped down the shaft and throughout the workings, but at this time electricity by armoured cable was also sent around the pit and below ground as well. Consequently either power source could have been used.

When an air compressor was working hard, great heat was given off through the metals; an outlet pipe took the air away into a large tank called the air receiver, and from there it went in large-diameter cast iron pipes down the shaft and along the passageways. The further it travelled, the smaller the pipe diameter was and so it powered many machines in various places above and below ground. Each fork in the pipe going down two passageways reduced the diameter, so from starting off at 10 inches, it reduced to 6 inches, then to 4 inches, later down to 3 inches, and even reducing to 2 inches at the far end of the pit. I was told by a mining engineer that the one drawback to a compressed air machine was the sound that it gave off, described as loud and piercing. By contrast, electricity makes little sound.

My friend and ex-pit deputy at Moston, Thomas Allen, could not confirm the use of compressed air on Slant 17 in his early years at the pit. He did know for certain that in the later years electricity was used to drive the later form of man-rider (rigged for silent running). Thomas remembers a large drum in a concrete engine house up above the slant, but memory can play tricks, for I saw no large drum in 1947. I could have missed seeing it, for my eyes would have been looking down for a firm secure footing as I climbed out of the grip. It would be an oversight though, for I did not miss much in those far off days. But the eyes only see what the brain decides to look for.

The Mystery Photograph

In our old family photograph album, between those marked 1926 and 1932, were a series of Moston Pit photographs taken in 1928/9. One other photograph was a couple of pages later, but unfortunately was undated, and for this reason shall always remain a mystery. The only certainty is that this photo alone was taken much later than the others that were dated. This important picture (Figure 46) shows two winding drums with their wires positioned in a wooden cradle, and standing at what appears to be the top of a Moston slant. This machine is not unique to the pit for at any date, each slant would have had a similar arrangement. What can be seen is not in anyway beautiful and certainly does not look state-of-the-art, at least through my eyes. I ask myself, why did my father take this picture of a machine that at the least looks its age?

One could see why he photographed the steam engine, or a unique section of passage in the pit. I suggest that whatever capacity my father held in the pit in that year of unknown date, he took this picture to make a point about the place, or because something special happened there at that spot. I strongly believe that it is the site of the accident at Slant 17 and, if so, dates the photograph to 1940. Perhaps he took it out of personal interest, or simply because he had not been at work on that fateful day, or perhaps Mr Richford, the General Manager, may have asked father to take one at the scene of the accident. My last thought might be that perhaps the Coroner requested one with regard to the five deaths?

Figure 46: "The Machine at the top of slant 17" soon after the accident (Photo T.Holliday).

There is no date or comment in the photo album to give us a clue, whereas all the other photographs had both date and place comments. The brake drum and brake band can be seen in the picture, but no visible power source; even the short brake handle can be seen pivoting on a horizontal bar, while the wires and their clips are visible in front of the drums. Thomas Allen told me that he did not remember a slant looking as in the photograph, but a coal pit is an ever evolving place. If things down below are altered for the better, the newer set up becomes the norm in no time at all and the detail as to how it was before soon fades and is easily forgotten. Changes would take place, executed by one set of miners from one age, and a later set of men would never have known things as they had been before. To be fair, Thomas Allen should know these places better than I knew them, for he worked down the pit for many years whereas I was only an occasional visitor to the place. However, I don't see my father taking any irrelevant pictures, under those alien, and very difficult conditions where flash powder could not be used. Obtaining a good picture from small gas testing lamps, depended for its success on a very long exposure which necessitated the use of a strong tripod to hold the camera firm. This image had to have a very special importance in the story of this pit and its history.

At the time that I am suggesting for this photograph, 1940, small electric accumulator lamps would have been carried and these had a good reflector to provide a fair beam of light. Father could have used the system called "painting with light" to light up the details better. The camera is set at open and the light from behind the camera is played slowly over the object that is required to be lit and photographed. Oldham Lamps, made these lamps for use in the pit. They were safe and took knocks well.

I don't know the date when safety headgear came to be used in the coal pits; before this time a woollen cap was the standard safety hat worn by most men. I remember in the lamp room when, with my father, I was fixed up with lamp and helmet prior to descending the pit, which might have been about 1946. Later, clever plastic ones came into more general use. By the time helmets were in regular use in the pit, the lamps were modified to fit on the helmet front, and so freed up the hand that held the older style lamp.

I maintain that this site in the pit was photographed for a special reason, and I suggest that the reason is the accident at Slant 17. Incidentally this way down by (Slant 17) led to the pit's most important coal, Big Seam, the Roger Coal. It is now for you, the reader, to judge if my theory will stand and can be accepted.

The long walk out

Very early in this book, I told of a small detour with my father through two sets of double air doors, along a short length of passage, and into the hot and smelly return airway for the pit. This passage did not exist in 1936, the time when the story, which I will now relate, occurred. However, it was probably this one set of events that brought to the management's notice the total inadequacy of an escape system, should anything go wrong in No. 3 shaft. I expect this short cut to safety was fashioned soon after the following event took place, for it was realised that the second way to safety for the Moston miners was far too long. In a worst case scenario, like an explosion or flood, or the engine in No. 3 shaft malfunctioning, speed of escaping from the scene is most important, and a long walk through the older parts of the pit is not what is required or ideal.

Thomas Allen told me this story. One of the pit blacksmiths had been fitting new slippers to the cage in No. 3 shaft whilst standing on the cage roof. This cage was at the surface, while the other cage was at the shaft bottom, 1,800 feet below. A slipper, is the metal fixture that slides down the shaft guide when the cage moves and is designed to stop the cages swinging about in the shaft. The blacksmith was wearing his regulation safety harness, but he suddenly slipped; the harness failed and he plummeted many hundreds of feet to his death below. He was doing nothing wrong, slippers were always fitted from the cage roof, and he wore the harness designed to stop him falling. This day, however, everything went wrong and the unthinkable happened. Because of the implications concerning this death in the shaft, a shaft that was having work done in it rather than being used for winding coal, the Inspector of Mines had to be called to the pit. This shaft could not be used again until he had investigated the accident and cleared the shaft for use.

Meanwhile the men working below, could not, under these circumstances, be brought up No. 3 shaft until the investigations were completed. Management structure moved into action, the phone lines from surface to the underground offices started humming and the Under Manager called all of his overmen from each district of the pit to meet with him for discussions. They had to determine their course of action for a successful evacuation of the pit. When the plan had been finalised, the pit deputies from each coal sector of the pit were summoned and were given the picture as to how the evacuation would be done. The men were then assembled, for it was close to the end of the afternoon shift; coal cutting was abandoned for the day, but no men could be wound up No. 3 shaft. The men were not told very much about the reason why work had stopped early, but rumours of the accident had started to filter through and this would have given the men a talking point as the long walk began.

It took a long time for all of the men from each district to reach the assembly point, some coming up from a great distance before they reached this point. The section of roadway used to gather the men together was the big one which ranged down from Mary Mine turn towards Major Mine (Figure 52). A head count would have been taken before each party left their own working district to ensure that no man was left behind. Some nameless leader, with knowledge of the older workings of the pit, led the miners down the roadway in the direction of the Major Seam workings, and into unknown places that most men in the pit had never seen.

The route became more involved and tortuous, the old wood props and heaps of fallen shale in places testifying to the age of these passages, fashioned out of rock at a much earlier time. It was a long tiring walk, but eventually the end came with a right turn into a passage hardly 5 feet high, through two tight fitting wooden doors. Now the first men stood in a railed passage that sloped away uphill, and from the hot draught, and that special pit smell, they knew they were in the return airway and heading for shaft No. 4. There was then a hold-up as those at the rear came on through, and there was some surprise when the men were told that many of these galleries had stood from 1890, when they were driven nearly 50 years before.

The men sat about talking in groups, and were relieved when at last the order was given to move on up, so in single file they moved off. It became steeper now, and the passage was unbelievably hot, due to the fact that the howling gale of hot air was passing them from behind, and didn't seem to provide any relief from the heat. Finally the passage widened into a sort of chamber and there, sitting between the rails on the floor, was a twelve-men-at-a-time man rider of six coaches. A normal man rider, in their experience, carried forty men in seven coaches, so looking at this one caused quite a laugh. An overman, as spokesman, went up to the front and in a matter-of-fact-voice he sternly warned the men: "lie flat as a pancake and don't move your head to look forward, or you may reach No. 4 shaft without it for the roof is very low". The miners laughed, but through the mirth they had got the message; this bit of equipment clearly came from an earlier age. The first men lay down on the equipment, a signal was sent and their feet slowly disappeared up into the dark of an ascending tunnel. These first men soon appreciated the truth of the overman's lecture as the roof seemed to pass at speed, just inches above their noses.

Eventually this fearful ride came to an end and they were able to stand up in the dark well that was No. 4 shaft bottom, thankful to have arrived safely in a much larger place. The cage for No. 4 stood close by and when enough men had arrived at this landing, they were whisked away to the surface and out to the day. Bell signals being used were three rings for men to be brought up, followed by one ring to ascend, the signal being repeated from those up at the top in No. 4's engine room. The men soon stepped out into a less familiar part of the pit yard.

Pit Chimneys and Lodges

If one sees a photograph of the pit, either the older pit or the new pits Nos 3 and 4, that has been taken from some distance away (see Figures 8 and 20), it is apparent that the tall, slim chimneys had an aesthetically pleasing streamlined top. I don't remember No. 2 pit on the Millfield, but certainly No. 1 pit chimney was exactly like the later No. 3 in design. Modern chimneys, the few that are still standing, have modern-built metal cowls to suit the form of power that they are serving, but they don't have the beauty of the old time brick chimneys. The modern cowls are perhaps designed to reduce the size of the chimney outlet, and I think some systems now have fans to push the heat and gasses away. The old Moston cowls had one sole purpose and that was to inhibit the entry of the wind into the top of the chimney which would create a down draught or a back pressure in the fire hole below. When we were young my friend Mike and I often sat and looked at these smoking stacks, for in truth many factories and mills had very similar chimneys themselves, especially on the Chadderton side of Oldham. This led us to wonder if Platts had supplied all of the similar ones after they had designed and patented their own shape and pattern, but this theory was not proven. We once discussed the top and wondered just how it was built; was it metal or was it of bricks. There was no way of knowing, for soot obscured the detail from our young searching eyes. It may be just our imagination, but we thought red bricks were used, stood upon or built up onto a girder pattern fixed across the mouth of the chimney. The girder pattern may have only had four quadrants, but we went away thinking that perhaps there were six? (see Figure 47). These old cowls were nick-named "a policeman's helmet" and had holes in the sides like a pepper pot to help disipate smoke (per Geoff Hayes). See Fig.28, p. 65.

Another important part of the steam-making process was an adequate supply of clean water for the boilers. According to a map from 1923, behind the Moston Mill was a large reservoir. I discount this as being anything to do with the older pit, No. 2, which was inundated, for I believe that this reservoir was built specially for the mill. However, just a short way southwest of the mill, towards Nuthurst Road, a smallish, odd-shaped lodge was situated with steep sides and deep looking water. I think I saw only part of it for if the older maps are studied a further part ran under what is now a school playing field. I think this lodge was the original for the Old Shaft on the Copthorn and No. 2 shaft of the earlier pit. After 1887 water would be pumped out of No. 2 shaft into this lodge and an underground pipe ran all the way down with gravity to fill up, and keep full the new lodge for pits Nos 3 and 4. The position of this lodge was behind the boiler house and against the fence that surrounded Ferranti's works. The overflow from this arrangement perhaps went under the railway and into the tunnel that took warm water into Moston Brook, the valley being called Boar Green Clough and mentioned earlier.

Historical Oddments

Historically, with all of the shafts at this pit, the desperate struggle to sink through 200 feet of glacial sands and clays that was left above the true rock surface, was the hardest and most dangerous part. In 1884 at the time of the flood in pits Nos 1-2, Mr Joseph Dickinson, a real fund of knowledge about the pits, for he had literally seen the inside of every one in the Lancashire Coalfield, was quoted as saying:

"when about 50 years ago, the late Mr Stanley succeeded in sinking his first shaft at Moston [this means the Old Shaft on the Copthorn] it was considered a great achievement, so many previous attempts having failed."

I never found written records of these attempts, nor at this time do I know much of the life of Mr Stanley, but I did read in a South Wales mining book a reference to the "sinking sands" met with at the sinking of the Moston Colliery. I do not know of any difference in sinking sand to ordinary sand, unless it be that the former has round grains like wind-blown sand, whereas the latter may have angular particles. The addition of water to the sand grains, however, puts them in motion as if the sand is a fluid rather than a solid, so that the sand can flow into a shaft bottom like water. The measures cut in the very first shaft at this pit were, after a time, recognized, and eventually the coals below were given names as at other pits at that time. Later, a sort of area-wide nomenclature emerged, so that the pit's own names could be used at each pit, but eventually names became more or less standardised across the coalfield.

As an example the coal called "Colonel" at Moston, known as "Ashton Great Seam" on geological maps and "Big Seam" at Moston, (named because of its thickness), eventually came to be known as the "Roger Coal". Unfortunately this name only held in the southeast Lancashire coalfield, for beyond the River Irwell it seems to have had another name, and uncertainty prevails. Confusion also arises by pits naming its coals by their thickness, as at Bower Colliery, calling it the "Bower 2 Foot Coal" while the official name for this coal is the "New Jet Amber". Moston never used this system, however.

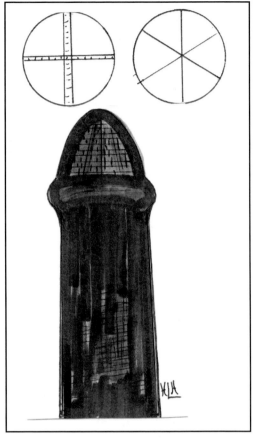

Figure 47: The cowl at the top of a Moston pit chimney.

Moston and Bradford Pits; the differences

After the flooding in the earlier pits, the new, deeper shafts (Nos 3 and 4) were sunk, and because of the experience already gained it was no surprise when each coal seam was cut through as the shaft was deepened. Because the new shafts were further south, due to the measures dipping, each coal was that bit lower than the same coal had been in the old pit. Because it was planned to go deeper, new coals were seen that had not been seen down in the older pit, but I do believe someone at the pit knew and understood the measures below, which are described as normal and standard for this part of the Lancashire coalfield. Even as late as the 1920s when work in the Platt mine had come to an end, a new exploratory tunnel going north found a new 4 feet thick coal, and it seemed to be expected for they called it the Black Seam, as in the Oldham area coalfield. The impression is that they knew it was there, and they went down determinedly to find it. There could have been an element of luck in the equation for at Bradford Colliery; for too many years the proprietors never seemed to know what part of the Coal Measures they were in, but I will start at the beginning.

I always thought of Bradford Colliery as Moston's twin, but except for being close to each other in mileage, not much is similar. The date of the earliest coal workings in this district are lost in the mists of time, and have left no written records, for mine owners at that date were extremely secretive about their work places. Parliament had to pass laws to force pits to make and share plans of their workings. The Bradford Colliery that I knew only existed for about sixty years, from 1904 to 1968 the period of modern mining. Earlier than this was the time of Mr Clegg Livesey and others and earlier still the colliery is understood to have been called Forge Pit. At least five shafts are present on this site at the pit and before shafts were in use there may have been levels; their mouths now lost and forgotten in the side of the Medlock Valley. The early worked coals beneath the pit site were at no great depth, the best seam (the Bradford 4 foot) lying at 337 feet below the surface dipping down deeper in a south westerly direction. Any pits before 1862 only required a single shaft to work its coal; the shaft for Forge Pit was unusual in that it was oval in shape, 9ft 6ins diameter at its widest, oval being perhaps more usual in metal mines. This old shaft was 155 yards (465 feet) deep, its depth covering all the coal seams known at that time at Bradford.

In about 1860 new, deeper coals were required, for the best coals had been worked out to the boundary. (Its coal area was limited by great faults that brought in the sandstone rocks.) An idea had long been held at Bradford that any deeper sinkings below the known coals, would progress into the Crombouke Series of coals, which were worked at pits west of the Irwell. This idea was based upon the presence of 4 feet thick coals at both places. The first shaft to try new, deeper measures was only a narrow one, the intention being to widen it if thicker coals were reached.

By 1866 this trial shaft was well down into new measures. However, it had not passed though any coals worth working and because of the slowness of progress in a narrow restricted shaft, at a depth of 434 yards (1,302 feet) below the 4 foot coal, the Diamond Rock Boring Company was contracted to finish the work. Only 24ft below, a fair coal seam measuring 3ft 2ins was reached which later came to be called the Parker Seam after R.T. Parker, the owner of Bradford. The depth from the surface to this coal is about 1,689 feet. Because no better coals had been seen during the drilling, this trial shaft was covered over, but not filled in.

Soon after 1900 the new Bradford Colliery was formed, centred on a new downcast shaft for the pit, and the Parker Shaft was uncovered and widened to18 feet in diameter. This then becoming the upcast shaft for this new pit. The deep shaft really was deep, its shaft bottom being set at 2,780ft 9ins in 1904, having found three good workable coal seams in the last 200 feet explored. Two of these had been worked at Moston pit for many years and if they had been recognized at Bradford for what they were, another 60 feet of sinking would have brought the new pit to perhaps the best seam in east Lancashire, the Roger Coal. Because of this oversight, some years later a 1,000 yard incline had to be made to harvest this coal at a later stage in the pit's history.

Probably the coming of the Geological Survey people in the 1920s made clear the place that this pit held in the overall picture of the Coal Measures. Gone was the dream of finding the Crumbouke coal seam, though they still used the name to rename one of their coals. Now for sure this pit's place was in the Oldham Coalfield; no longer did they think they belonged in the measures as at Swinton and Pendlebury. Now for the first time the sense of uncertainty cleared, and the succession at Bradford Colliery was understood. The old, shallow coal seams that had provided coals for over 200 years had not been seen in other areas of Lancashire for nowhere else were these Coal Measures present; only Bradford had these coals, the Bradford Coal Group.

Lying 1,689 feet below surface, the Parker Coal is thought to be equivalent to the Worsley 4 Foot Mine known west of the Irwell. The deep shaft of 1904 stopped at 2,780 feet below the surface, and the new coals for this pit were at 2,581 to be called "Top Mine" and were the same as the Major Mine at Moston, with the next good coal at 2,682 feet down called the Middle Mine. The lowest coal was at 2,770 feet below the surface and given the name the Deep Mine, this being called Colonel at Moston and also at Ashton Moss Pit. Many changes took place over the pit's last 30 years of work: changes of ownership, changes in output per week, changes in areas of coal cutting, and eventually came nationalisation and the N.C.B. Older pits were closed down with millions of pounds being spent to modernise Bradford Colliery, all to no avail. Its coals were so clean that the pit did not have enough stone of its own to support the roof after the coal had been taken out. So by 1968, the super pit of the coalfield was closed down forever and only memories now remain.

It is a fact that at Bradford Colliery, the geothermal gradient was quite low, considerably lower than the pits on the west side of the Irwell in the West Manchester coalfield. Unlike at Moston, which was considered a wet pit, Bradford was very dry, and this can easily be explained by the fact that the shallower a pit is, the wetter that pit is. Put another way, the Moston shaft cut through the Colonel Seam at 1,213 feet down, whereas at Bradford that same coal was not seen until the shaft was down to 2,769 feet, so there would be less water permeating through the rock at Bradford, the deeper pit. The difference in thickness of measures from the surface down to this coal was about 1,500 feet which is very nearly the whole depth of Moston's shaft. Faulting has caused this difference; the block of land on which Bradford Colliery stood has preserved 1,500 feet of higher layers, but at Moston these 1,500 feet have been weathered away by wind, rain, and ice in the glacial period.

In 1935 the pit at Bradford was bought by the Manchester Collieries Co. and from then on productivity improved. The Roger Seam was opened out, and certainly now Bradford was able to mine more coal in a given time than at Moston. Later on, long term plans were made to wind skips in the Parker Shaft (the Upcast) after it had been deepened to a similar depth to the Deep Shaft; this occurred after 1946-1948 when its depth had reached 2,865 feet. A state-of-the-art Koepe Winder of the friction wheel-type was built at Metropolitan Vickers in Trafford Park to bring up the skips carrying 12 tons each; shaft strengthening took place and a new reinforced concrete headgear was built that stood 200 feet high. The deep shaft was also improved at this time.

The top quality coal from both Bradford and Moston collieries, being so hard, came out of the pits very clean, so little washing had to be done before sale. Soon after the National Coal Board took over the pits, the areas of coal yet unmined at Moston and at Ashton Moss Colliery were given over to Bradford Colliery and both the other pits were soon closed. However, Bradford's policy of taking coal from under the city forced its early closure within sixteen years of Moston. This left uncut reserves said to be 310 million tons. Part of Bradford Collieries workings were at the great depth of over 4,000 feet below the surface.

Geologically these two pits were never twins and the only things in common was a mutual ventilation tunnel running between them and the good quality of their coals.

The Shared Ventilation Tunnels

After 1950, when Moston Colliery had been closed, it was suggested that Bradford Colliery could soon be cutting coal under the area that had stood in reserve for Moston, and lay between the two pits. This never came to pass, for Bradford had been taking coal from underneath the city for so long, that too much was at stake to move to another area. A new district for coal cutting was prepared, however, under the 5 miles of country between the pit at Bradford and those last two pits still at work in Oldham, Woodpark and Oak Pits. This plan allowed these two pits to be shut down and their coals gathered from Bradford by the Oldham miners. Much money was spent on modernisation at Bradford Colliery to cut new coals in a new safe district away from the city with its bridges and high buildings.

Sorry to say at Bradford there was no spare land to store vast tonnages of coal, so it was trucked away to Ashton Moss Pit where there was spare storage space. In 1946 Platts were to convert for skip winding the upcast shaft No. 4. It was sheathed in concrete ready for shaft deepening, but talk of nationalisation soon put a stop to any plans for the future. One skip capable of holding 8 or 12 tons of coal is easily dealt with in loading from a hopper, whereas the separate loading of many small mine trucks holding the same tonnage of coal would be a most difficult and time consuming exercise. The reasons for this plan was less manhandling and more coal wound quickly to the surface. Naturally the plan was dropped when talk of nationalisation began, and no more development work was done.

Had Platts stayed in control, Moston Pit was set to become a most modern pit; vast tonnages would have been wound at both of its shafts, and the new area of extraction was in a place that had never had coal mined from before, this being under the district of Lightbowne. The manager at that time stated that 100 years supply awaited including the intact Roger Mine Coal. The coal under Moston and Bradford pits was said to be the best in the country. No mineworker in these two pits ever imagined what would happen to their jobs and indeed the whole coal industry in those next few years.

During the later years at Moston Pit, in National Coal Board times, a system of long ventilation tunnels were instigated. I know for certain that one main tunnel was connected from Bradford to Moston's return airway, but it just could have been linked after Moston shut down, for Thomas Allen, the pit Deputy, never saw or heard of this tunnel before the pit closed. Electricians from Bradford were detailed to walk through as far as Moston to check for electrical problems in the wiring, as well as checking for falls of roof or walls, It is understood that this roadway was secured only with wooden props, not iron girders, and it was less well protected against collapses. For a number of years after Moston closed down, the ventilation in No. 4 shaft at Moston was kept working for the good of Bradford and its airflow. I was told that other ventilation tunnels went from Moston to Ashton Moss Colliery. An extra large one ran from there, back to Bradford, making a ventilation triangle, and a separate tunnel which started from Ashton Moss Colliery ran to two pits in the Oldham area called Woodpark and Oak collieries. Combined ventilation tunnels give the advantage of more ways to escape in the case of an emergency underground.

MOSTON COLLIERY

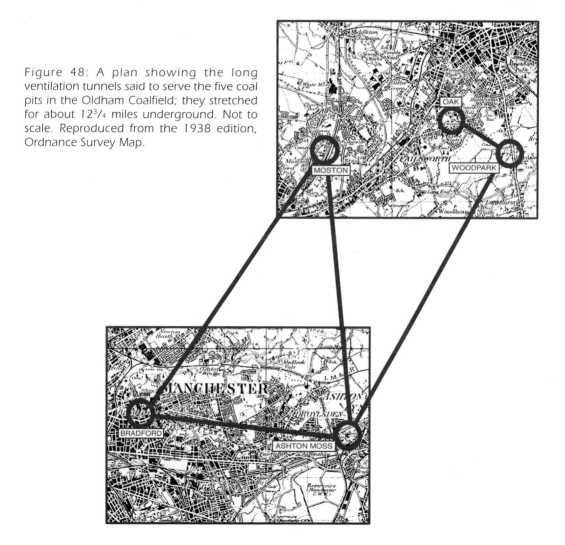

Figure 48: A plan showing the long ventilation tunnels said to serve the five coal pits in the Oldham Coalfield; they stretched for about $12^3/_4$ miles underground. Not to scale. Reproduced from the 1938 edition, Ordnance Survey Map.

No. 4 Shaft (the upcast)

This shaft worked like an 1,800 foot high chimney to clear the bad air from the passageways below. If these mutual ventilation tunnels did exist, the following would be their approximate mileage:

Bradford Colliery to Moston Colliery	2½ miles
Bradford Colliery to Ashton Moss Colliery	3¼ miles
Moston Colliery to Ashton Moss Colliery	3¼ miles
Ashton Moss Colliery to Woodpark Colliery	2¾ miles
Woodpark Colliery to Oak Colliery	1 mile
Total approximate mileage underground	12¾ miles

So Moston's No. 4 shaft became an important player in the last few years of some of the coal pits in the southeast Lancashire coalfield, a key role still valued by the other surviving pits, which at that time felt they would work on secure for many more years to come. Bradford Colliery had many millions of pounds spent on it to bring it up to a productive and modern standard. Production figures rose from 171,557 tons in 1937, to 243,363 tons by 1940. Then in N.C.B. times the sky was the limit, for the Roger Mine was at last in full flow, by a now well mechanised pit. But 2,800 feet above, bridges were cracking and factories were putting in large claims for compensation caused by the mining under the city of Manchester. Solid stowing of the goafs (the open spaces where coal has gone from) was envisaged, but never came to pass, for these east Lancashire coals were so clean and solid, that there was no dirt parting or waste rock spare to pack in the goafs. When foreign dirt had to be brought in from other pits to fill up the holes, the writing was on the wall for Bradford Colliery, and the large reserve of quality coal was never completely extracted. Bradford Colliery shut 18 years after Moston Colliery had closed down.

Figure 49: Photograph of the pit in 1946 from the Failsworth Golf Course just before nationalisation. Note that the upcast shaft (No. 4) has been encased in concrete ready for conversion to skip winding by Platt Bros Holdings.

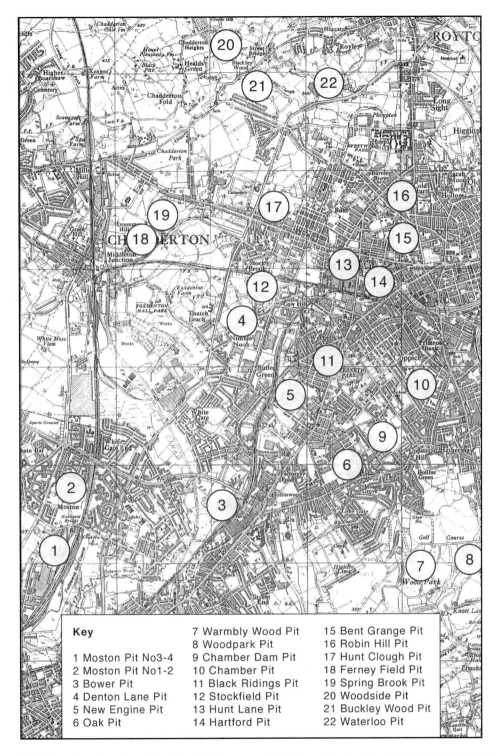

Key

1 Moston Pit No3-4	7 Warmbly Wood Pit	15 Bent Grange Pit
2 Moston Pit No1-2	8 Woodpark Pit	16 Robin Hill Pit
3 Bower Pit	9 Chamber Dam Pit	17 Hunt Clough Pit
4 Denton Lane Pit	10 Chamber Pit	18 Ferney Field Pit
5 New Engine Pit	11 Black Ridings Pit	19 Spring Brook Pit
6 Oak Pit	12 Stockfield Pit	20 Woodside Pit
	13 Hunt Lane Pit	21 Buckley Wood Pit
	14 Hartford Pit	22 Waterloo Pit

Figure 50: Map showing the pits of the Oldham area including Moston's two phases of working. Bradford Colliery is about 2¹/₂ miles away to the southwest and nearer the city of Manchester. Reproduced from the 1950 Ordnance Survey Map.

Returning to Moston Colliery to finish off this story, the most alert readers among you may have noticed that in my text I have made little mention of shaft No. 4, and this is because I never knew much about it. I never travelled in its cage, which was the emergency way out if the need ever arose. The hot and dry return airway that I was once taken to told me little if anything about the 1,200 feet of apparently ever steepening passage that led to the base of the shaft. No. 4 shaft was only 615 feet deep; the fan chamber at its top I was shown in my youth, but was quite glad to hasten away from its noise and draught at the first chance to seek a quieter place. At this time of my life in about 1947, the top of the upcast shaft (No. 4) had been swathed in concrete ready for the shaft deepening to begin, but this was not pursued due to the coming of nationalisation. Double doors would control the way in to the cage to preserve the efficiency of the ventilation, the bad air being drawn away by the fan.

After 1950 when Moston Colliery was closed down, the ventilation that had worked so well over the years was kept working for the other collieries in the system. Woodpark and Oak collieries received the benefit from Moston No. 4 pit's ventilation plant, but were both closed down themselves by 1955 and 1956. Ashton Moss worked on until 1959 and Bradford closed in1968.

The following shows the approximate bearing of the ventilation tunnels between Moston, Bradford and Ashton Moss and the last two pits in the Oldham Area:

MOSTON TO BRADFORD	195°
MOSTON TO ASHTON MOSS	137°
WOODPARK TO ASHTON MOSS	195°
BRADFORD TO ASHTON MOSS	96°
OAK TO WOODPARK PIT	120°

Locomotives for Hauling Coal

For at least 50 years, Moston Colliery had its own shunting engine and a complex of sidings with delivery lines stretching away about 1,200 feet up to Moston Mill. This complex of sidings angled down to join the main line from Manchester Victoria to Yorkshire, with some storage sidings beyond the main line below the golf course. There was also a coal yard below the Malleable Castings Factory, with rails to service it with coal, delivered by the pit locomotive, and in the years before the coming of the railway, horses and carts would have done the same job. I shall give some facts about Moston's locomotives and freely admit some speculation on my part.

It has been rumoured that a number of locomotives have been owned and used by the pit. How many is still at question. As a youth of about 13 years, a memory remains very clear of seeing the pit engine shut up for the night in its rectangular engine shed, dampers closed down so as to keep the fire in all night, the shed gate locked up, but the smoke drifting up from the line of the roof. Next morning the driver would be in to open up the damper, and in no time this little worker would be alive again and moving away to its work.

It has been said in the book *The Moston Story* (Fr Brian Seale 1984), that the pit locomotive was called *Robin Hood*. I can't argue with this for at least two were built and given this name. The earliest was a 0-4-0 Saddle-Tank engine built by Black Hawthorn in 1893, works No. 1038. The cylinders were 14 inch bore, with a 19 inch stroke, and the wheel diameter was 4 feet. It worked at 140 psi pressure and weighed 28 tons. It was said to have been bought new in 1893 by the Clifton and Kearsley Coal Co., but returned to Chapman and Ferneaux (Black Hawthorn's successors) in 1901.

The second *Robin Hood*, a 0-4-0 Saddle Tank engine, was built by Chapman and Ferneaux at Gateshead in 1901, works No. 1,200. The cylinders were 14 inch bore, with a 19 inch stroke, with coupled wheels of 3 feet 2 inch diameter and a working pressure of 140 psi, with a weight of 23 tons. It is said that this, the second engine of the same name, was built new for its owners, Clifton and Kearsley Coal Co. I speculate that the first *Robin Hood* was sent back faulty, and this second locomotive became a replacement for the earlier one. What year, if ever, it came to work at Moston is anyone's guess and the engine was not scrapped until December 1961. If Moston Colliery ever owned this engine, Platts must have got it second-hand or rented it on loan from Clifton and Kearsley Coal Co. Again I speculate on some form of partnership, or at least co-operation, between Platts and the Clifton and Kearsley Company. In the publication *Just Henry* (Bairsto 1991) there is a picture of a Moston Colliery shunting engine (photographed in about 1900). I am no expert and I don't doubt it is an authentic Moston engine, but I do doubt the date for in 1900 the engine would have only 4 wheels as a 0-4-0, but this photo shows 6 wheels making it an 0-6-0 and therefore later than 1900. A date of around 1907 would seem more probable.

The next engine and this certainly had connections with Moston Colliery, was called *Failsworth*. Hayes (2004) shows that this was an 0-6-0 saddle tank engine, built by Hawthorn, Leslie in 1907, works No. 2,727. The cylinders were 15-inch bore by 22-inch stroke, and it had coupled wheels of 3ft 9in diameter. Its working pressure was 160 psi and it weighed 30 tons. As far as can be determined, Platt Brothers Holdings bought *Failsworth* new, so this engine worked at Moston pit for 43 years until the pit was closed down in 1950. Clifton Hall Colliery site, down in the valley of the Irwell, was still being used as a coal washing plant at that time. Their locomotive called *Pecket* was coming to the end of its useful working life and for its last stint was transferred to Outwood Colliery in late 1949. With the closure of Moston in 1950, the good (if long-lived) shunting engine *Failsworth* was sent to replace *Pecket* at Clifton Hall Colliery, where it worked on until 1958 at which time it was scrapped.

Westwood also belonged to Platt Brothers Holdings and is said to have come from Moston Colliery. However, it is difficult to envisage the pit requiring two engines at any one time, so one must assume that this second engine worked the sidings near to Platt Brothers factories in or around Hartford Works in Oldham, this being the centre of Platt's engineering operations. Built by Hudswell Clarke in 1913, works No. 1,036, its specifications were: cylinders 16-inch bore by 24-inch stroke, coupled wheels 3ft 7ins in diameter, weight 32 tons, and it worked at a pressure of 160 p.s.i.

The story is told that it was unique in being driven from the left hand side of the foot plate, this born out in the photograph published in *Just Henry* (Bairsto 1991) for the driver stands at the left window. In 1956, this engine went to Clifton Hall Colliery as 'Failsworth' had done before. However, during 1957 an underground tunnel was being driven to connect the two pits of Newtown with Wheatsheaf Colliery, so that all the coal from both pits could be wound up at Wheatsheaf. This then required an increase in rail traffic so *Westwood* from Oldham was one of three engines sent to do this work. *Westwood* was the old boy of the three, and as both pits closed by 1961 they were pensioned off and sent to the Walkden yard, *Westwood* being scrapped in 1968.

The photograph in *Just Henry*, referred to earlier, was probably of *Failsworth*, for this one alone was a 0-6-0 as seems to be the case in the photograph, whereas *Westwood* and the two *Robin Hoods* were only 0-4-0s. For a great number of years these tireless little workers served Platts the company and Moston the colliery very well, but after nationalisation, the day of the pit and the steam locomotive were severely limited. I think its quite amazing how long a good, steam driven, pit winding engine, or a pit locomotive, could run without wearing out; only the coming of new technology brought change and a newer, but not necessarily better, form of power. (See Hayes 2004 for further details.)

The *Failsworth* seen here at Clifton Hall Sidings on 10 february 1951 after its arrival from the closed Moston Colliery. © Mr. G. Hayes

The Final days of Moston Colliery

In the late 1940s the pit was less settled than it had been. Platt Brothers had sold out to the Manchester Collieries Group who had a great track record behind them in the coal pits of Lancashire, but were not at Moston long enough to do any good in the field of development and modernisation. Nationalisation of the coal pits was certainly coming soon and when the Coal Board took control, output was adjusted to improve profitability.

Figure 51: The pit from beyond Broadway in its last year, 1950.

The men cutting coal were exhorted to keep beating their targets or the pit would be shut, and this kind of thing does not make work a happy place. The steepness of the coal seams had not allowed many of the modern mining improvements to come to this pit; remember it had the steepest coals in the whole of Lancashire. The spin-off from this was that Moston continued to mine its coal in the old fashioned way, for the modern way would not work with such steep gradients. As suggested above, what would be rated as good production figures at one time will not suffice in the years to come. If no new techniques are introduced into the pit then production remains static. When the National Coal Board took over in 1947 the whole emphasis was on increased tonnages or the pit would have to close, and because of the difficulties outlined, the required production figures were never attained. Closure of the pit was announced, and the men who had been used to work at this pit, and who had felt at ease working here, were strangely unnerved at the thought of being sent to work at another pit.

On the 17th of May 1950, as a protest over the threat of closure of their pit, 340 day shift workers went below at their allotted time, but resolved to stay down for as long as they could, armed only with one day's sandwiches and some liquid refreshment. It can now be said that their determination exceeded their strength. A coal pit near 2,000 feet deep is a hot place in which to strike and so they were soon sharing the drinks, the little that was left, rationing the liquids to conserve their strength. Up on the surface a representative of the National Coal Board refused to send down any water or food to the men below. Resolve started to weaken a little and in order to conserve further liquid, some of the haulage and maintenance men, together with the young trainees and the older men of the pit, gave what was left of their provisions to the rest and ascended up to the surface.

Twenty four hours had now passed; inactivity and the slow passage of time started to gnaw at their resolve and after two full days below 170 men came back up to the light. Nothing was gained, it now appears, with this gesture of defiance from the men.

On the 5th of June 1950 Moston Colliery closed, this working place extinguished and its machinery silent for the very first time in 130 years. The life in Moston Pit, a living, breathing, working place, was extinguished forever; a place that had seen heroic struggles, a place of strong friendships between men, and where the very best was brought out at times of adversity. At the time of closure there were still 8 working faces producing coal of good quality, for the pit had always been able to sell as much coal as it could bring to the surface.

The greatest asset at this pit was its reserves; these remained untapped and were given to another pit and were said to be enough to last for another 120 years at the 1946 production figures. The No. 4 shaft with its superb ventilation machinery was kept extracting for the benefit of the other pits in the ventilation triangle, still operating until 1961 at which time only Bradford Colliery remained open. Workers then built concrete dams to seal off the passageways both sides of both shafts and these great voids were filled. It is impossible to know how many thousands of tons of best quality coal came up No. 3 shaft in the 63 years of its working life. The very last time that I saw where the shaft had been, its place was marked by the thick wire rope that still came up out of its circle. This same cable, this lifeline from the past, became a way back for my thoughts, so that now I can walk again with my father through the roadways and crosscuts of his pit, and I see it again unchanged, just as it was 50 years before.

The Quiet Pit

My engine now is still and cold,
No water does my boiler hold,
No more is coal a valued ore,
My days producing, now no more.

My headgear's wheels no longer speed,
No more a driver's hand they need,
No hiss of steam when cage goes down,
For now no men work underground.

Air to ventilate, no more required,
Boilers for steam are never fired,
Those ponies in the field at play,
May just wonder who'll bring their hay.

H.L.Holliday

The recollections of Pit Deputy Mr Thomas Allen

Memory is a strange thing. We have the ability to remember in graphic detail many things that were of great interest to us in earlier times, but are unaware of the process that slowly alters some of those details, and the changes, though slight, become an integral part of those ongoing memories. Having visited the bottom of Moston Colliery only a small number of times, and these over fifty years ago, I was very happy when Mr Thomas Allen, a former Pit Deputy, offered his reminiscences to me for inclusion. He walked the roadways of the pit for over 17 years and knew the tunnels like the back of his hand. Here then is his description and I am glad to say that except for one minor place down below, his recollections fit well with my memories:

"In these brief notes I will try to explain by diagram the work done to extract coal, but first the descent. The cage was two tiered, (i.e. one compartment above the other) and when filled with men, the Banksman would ring down to the Onsetter as well as to the Winding engine room from where the signal was repeated. The cage then slowly begins to descend, then suddenly 'Whush' – bungy jumping or free fall from an aeroplane has nothing on this journey; it was as if the bottom had dropped out of the cage. [If he never got used to this sensation, what chance us the occasional visitor. As the cage begins to slow your body gets very heavy and a weakness comes into the legs.]

A great surprise awaits you as you step out of the cage at shaft bottom; the height of the large passage in front and its width. It has electric lights, and all the walls and the roof are lime washed; this increases the brightness. The main roadway at shaft bottom runs west to east; turning right proceeding eastwards there is a large engine room with a huge drum inside; this engine powers a haulage rope along the floor as far as the Colonel Mine at the far end of the pit. The rope is endless; haulage hands with clip and chain fit empty tubs onto this rope to be sent further into the mine in relays, and full tubs come back holding 10 cwt. in each tub. Incidentally, the endless rope runs through pulleys and wheels to keep the rope at the correct height for the trucks and to help it to run round corners. [Each coal seam in the pit is given a name followed by the word mine, and this is standard practice in Lancashire. However for clarity in this book I use the word seam as well as its name, rather than mine, but I leave Thomas's pages just as he wrote them down so as not to spoil the flavour of his text.]

The first mine that we come to is called Mary Mine and the miners' pet name for it is Fossil Mine because of the wealth of fossils seen near and in the coal seam. Some were of fish, some were unmistakably of shells; fossil ferns have also been seen as well as something that looked just like the branches of young fir trees. The Mary Mine was served by pit ponies which took in the empty tubs and these, when filled with coal, were pulled back to the main roadway and the ponies then took into the mine more empties. The main roadway after Mary Mine swung to the south; it was a dual road – the empties along one side and full tubs along the other – with a good walking space between for the miners. The next mine down this road to the left was Foxholes 1 and 2; these faces were the last faces at Moston to be opened up for working before closure. All road and airways were steel arched, the main brow being 18ft high and 20ft wide.

My duties as a Deputy at Foxholes 1 were many and varied; my priorities in the job were to ensure the smooth running of my district with the first priority being safety, and output coming second. In a Deputy's report, which was completed daily, but kept at the surface for twelve months and one day, I had to enter conditions in my sector – shortages of materials, gas readings and their percentages, details about any accidents or incidents and I had to sign this report together with my Overman. First aid at Moston Colliery was excellent. Within ten minutes of an accident the first aid man was down below and on his way to the scene. In every separate district was kept a first aid box, which was replenished on a weekly basis; in each was kept everything from a $\frac{1}{2}$ inch bandage, to slings and splints, and tourniquets as well. There was always on call a person who had had first aid instruction who could rush to the scene of an accident. As said earlier, any accident in my sector had to be entered in to the Deputy's Report for the day.

As we leave Foxholes Mine behind, the main tunnel continues through very hard rock for something like 100 yards to Big Mine turn still heading south. To go to Big Mine one would turn left, easterly in direction, but more of this later. Continuing south leads to the workings of the Major Mine; the coal from this mine is conveyed by ponies as in Mary Mine. At about 70 yards on, we come to a very large fossilised tree trunk, still standing in a vertical position completely replaced by stone; two men, standing finger to finger could just about encircle it. If we continued ahead towards Major Mine we would be heading in the general direction of Failsworth. Returning to Big Mine and turning to the east, we soon come to the now notorious No. 17 slant on our right; this was the steep brow fitted with a man rider and the scene of a fatal accident. [See 'Accidents in the Pit, p. 91.] Slant 17 continues in a southerly direction heading for the area called Daisy Nook where the Roger Coal was mined. Up on the surface just past the lower end of the slant stood the double mill called the Marlborough Mill; it was forbidden by law to mine any coal from below this mill. [This then clearly places Slant 17 under the lower end of Broadway in Failsworth; it had an incline of 1 in 3° and was 900 feet long to where it leveled out again and continued in a southerly direction.]"

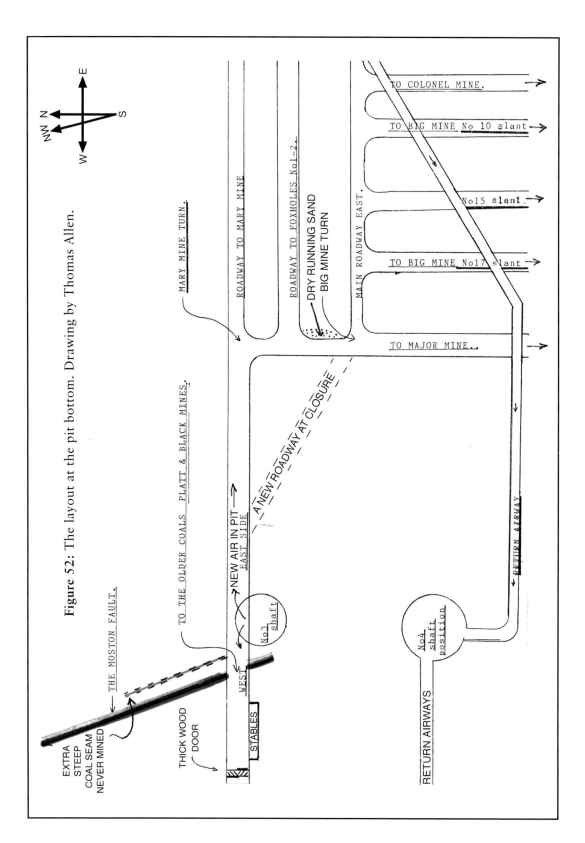

Figure 52: The layout at the pit bottom. Drawing by Thomas Allen.

[Thomas says that all that he has spoken of before, was to the east side of shaft No. 3. What he describes next was west of this same shaft.] On the west side of pit bottom are the stables; the ponies were looked after by an Ostler who groomed and washed them, and fed and watered them, generally looking after their welfare. On annual holidays the ponies were brought up to the surface to be let into the field belonging to the pit, alongside St Mary's Road. Many people thought because these ponies work in the dark for so many months of the year they must be blind. [This is not so, but for protection their eyes were shielded from bright light for a day or so, to let their eyes adjust when newly come to the surface.] Whilst down below, at the precise time of the ending of the ponies' shift, without any prompting from the men, they just took themselves off, passing the pit bottom and into their own stable. Before the stables, after passing No. 3 shaft, but in the right hand wall could be seen the large Moston Fault. Close to this fault, a fine seam of coal rears up, parallel to the fault. This thick coal was investigated in the days when this pit was still young, but it was concluded that the coal was at much too steep an angle to set timbers in so it was never worked.

Thomas told me of the thick wooden doors beyond the stables, but he had never been through them and knew nothing of what lay beyond. I think that the two coals not known by him, were first found west of the doors. Platt seam (i.e. the Oldham Great Mine) was found before 1890. Black Mine seam of the Oldham Coalfield was found from cross measure tunnels driven from the Platt Mine in the early1920s. The main tunnel going west was given the name of Platt Tunnel, and the main tunnel going east, was called the Hardman Tunnel. Both tunnels turned to the south to explore new ground after 1887. Finally Thomas said that in his working time, all coal was extracted on the same principle as he shows in his drawings, and at every seam in the pit.

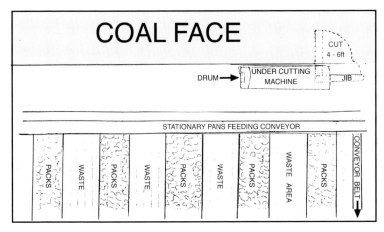

Figure 53: How we cut the coal. Drawing (not to scale) by Thomas Allen. It starts off always at the bottom of the coal face after first being pinned down with pit props and anchored to the floor and roof to keep the cutter steady. Next, the jib with two sets of teeth is set in motion. The jib moving in an arc cuts under the coal until the jib has cut for 90° degrees. Now at a right angle to the coal, it can be locked in that position; the steel rope attached to the cutter is now hauled up the face for 30 to 40 yards and anchored to the floor. The machine is then set in motion, and a revolving drum winds in the cable as the cutter cuts and moves up the sloping face, undercutting all the way. Next a driller drills boreholes approximately 4ft 6ins apart at an angle, then the shotfirer packs the holes with 8 oz of powder and a detonator for each hole. At this time the men retire to a safe place and the charges are fired. The coal is blown down and the men spade the broken coal into pans and with the help of gravity, and the odd push now and again, the coal slides down and drops onto a moving conveyer belt and so outbye. The word pan refers to a number of lengths of metal, shaped something like a children's banana slide, their sheer weight being the limiting factor. A number of them are fitted together making a long line and because Moston coal seams are so steep, gravity aids in the coal's delivery to the conveyer.

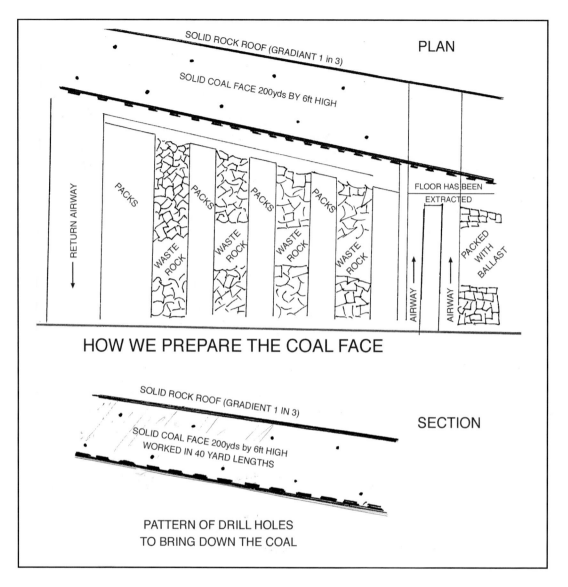

PLAN

SOLID ROCK ROOF (GRADIANT 1 in 3)

SOLID COAL FACE 200yds BY 6ft HIGH

RETURN AIRWAY

PACKS

PACKS

PACKS

PACKS

WASTE ROCK

WASTE ROCK

WASTE ROCK

WASTE ROCK

FLOOR HAS BEEN EXTRACTED

AIRWAY

AIRWAY

PACKED WITH BALLAST

HOW WE PREPARE THE COAL FACE

SOLID ROCK ROOF (GRADIENT 1 IN 3)

SECTION

SOLID COAL FACE 200yds by 6ft HIGH WORKED IN 40 YARD LENGTHS

PATTERN OF DRILL HOLES
TO BRING DOWN THE COAL

Figure 54: How we prepare the coalface. Drawing (not to scale) by Thomas Allen. This diagram shows the coalface as if from above; the coal at this stage is ready for blasting down. The coal face is the area above the dark line, shown on the plan and the line indicates where the coal has been undercut to a depth of 4ft 6ins. The undercut is shown by a dashed line. The dots in the lower section show the positions of the drillholes in the coal face; the area between the two roadways is well supported by built up stone and packed waste.

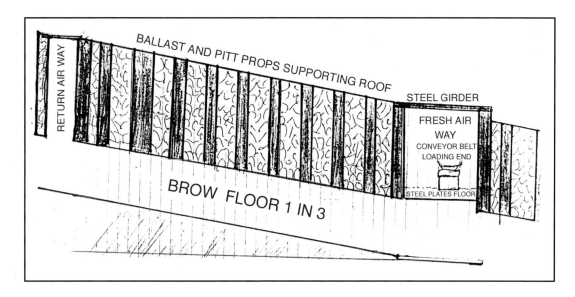

Figure 55: The approaches to the working face. Drawing (not to scale) by Thomas Allen. The following is a section showing details of the approaches to the coal face. The main roadway holds the conveyer which takes the coal away to be loaded into tubs at another place. Another roadway is visible at a higher level and this is the return airway for this sector of the pit. The area that I marked Ballast and Pit Props, support the roof to allow the men safe working space. Now that the coal has been taken, this space will become the goaf. However the passageways are made very secure so that they can stand safely for a number of years. The coal has been followed to deeper levels, generally in a southerly direction, the cut coal being always extracted eastwards.

Thomas Holliday of Moston Colliery; an Epilogue

Thomas Holliday, my father, worked as Overman at Moston Colliery and may also have been the Under-Manager for some years, though I have no proof of this. He was born at Aspatria in Cumberland, 24 October 1901.

He attended the Nelson School at Wigton before starting work at his local pit, and while at school he chose to play Rugby Union rather than the alternative, Cricket. Coming from a family of six children he was the second youngest of five brothers and one sister.

The first pit that he worked at was called Brayton Domain No. 5, at Aspatria in Cumberland, and his father, my grandfather, had worked many years there also. This pit was in the valley below the ridge where most of his village was situated. After working some time at this pit, he decided to attend a school of mining to take some examinations and perhaps to gain promotion. Manchester being the place for work on the west side of Britain, and also on a nearly direct railway line, he took the steam train, and so secured work at Moston Colliery. He worked on the early shift, and I do mean early, so that he could attend his classes on mining later in the day. The year would have been perhaps 1926. Some time later he passed his Under-Manager's Certificate, but worked on at Moston rather than go back up north.

When the Second World War started I was six years old and rather than be evacuated to live with strangers, as children of the cities were at the start of the war, I was sent to live with my grandma at Aspatria. In about 1942, so that we could become a family again, father transferred to Gillhead pit, near Flimby on the Cumberland coast, and took up his position as the Under-Manager there. The vista from this pit, situated high on the hill, when looking across the Solway Firth to Scotland was quite majestic, but it was a cold and windy place. The moment that you reached the shaft top, the ceaseless wind tore at a miner's shirt ! About 1945 we all moved back to Moston, my father resuming his job at the pit once more, but by this time a friend from former times had gone from the pit office and things were never quite the same again. Mr Herbert Richford, the General Manager, who had served the pit and Platt Brothers for so many working years, was no longer there. My father felt that he would like to take up teaching and in October of 1946 took up the post as an instructor at a Staff Training College situated at Nuneaton in the Midlands. He held this position until 16 April 1948, but did not enjoy being away from home, returning only at weekends, nor did he want to move and set up home in another place. His new job was as Supervisor at a Government Training Centre for youths who wanted to find work in the pits. This he did from a Training Centre which he started at a still producing pit, Oak Colliery in Hollinwood, near to Oldham. The surface buildings were used for teaching purposes and of course there were shafts, three in total at this pit, and dark passageways below, where his boys were instructed in safe working practices. Thomas and his team worked well, and he was happy during his time at Oak Colliery.

In about 1952 the National Coal Board asked my father if he would start a similar unit for them, west of the Irwell, for the pits that had once belonged to the Manchester Collieries group. In accepting this, his new place of work moved to Newtown Colliery at Swinton and Pendlebury. With Newtown as his teaching base, he had to liaise with other groups at Sandhole (once called the Bridgewater Colliery) as well as with Cleworth Hall.

On January 4th 1956 my father came home from work early, feeling most unwell, and died on January 11th 1956 aged 55 years. The following obituary and photograph are taken from volume 3, number 7 of "OUTLOOK" (1956, National Coal Board):

"Death of Mr Tom Holliday
It is with regret that we learn of the death of Mr Thomas Holliday, the manager of Newtown Training Centre, who died suddenly on the 11 January 1956. After having trained in the Cumberland Coalfields, Mr Holliday worked underground for 20 years and subsequently held the positions of a Supervisor at a government training centre, a Training Officer with the Manchester Collieries, and an Instructor at a Staff Training College, where he lectured on discussion methods until he took up an appointment as the Manager at the Newtown Training Centre, after a period as the Manager of the Oak Colliery Training Centre which is in the Oldham Coalfield."

Figure 56: T. Holliday, my father (Photo H.L. Holliday).

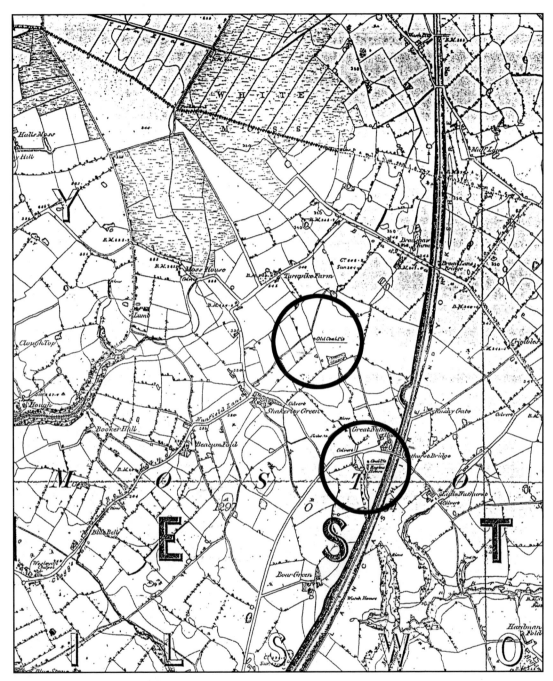

Figures 57: An Ordnance Survey Map of the area of the pit, dated 1848, showing Shaft No. 1, marked Coal Pit and Engine House (lower circle) with the position of the Old Shaft marked, Old Coal Pit (upper circle). Reproduced from the 1848 Ordnance Survey Map.

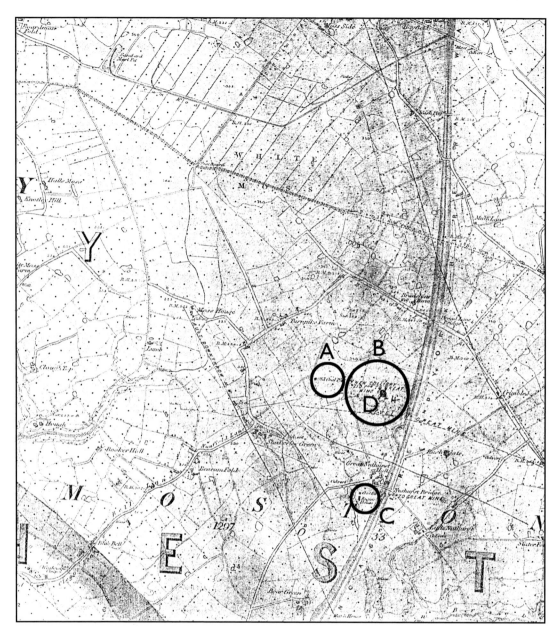

Figure 58: A Geological Survey Map of the area of the pit, dated 1863, showing No.1 Pit marked Coal Pit and Engine House as before (B), plus the details, 285 yards to Great Mine (C). The site of the Old Shaft is marked Old Coal Pit (A), and not far from it, a spot is marked New Colliery 210 yards to Great Mine. This being the site of the No. 2 shaft which was completed in 1850. This map shows borehole marked No. 4 (D) and shows proof that Mr Stanley's Old Shaft on the Copthorn did exist. Extract courtesy of the British Geological Survey 1st Edition 1863.

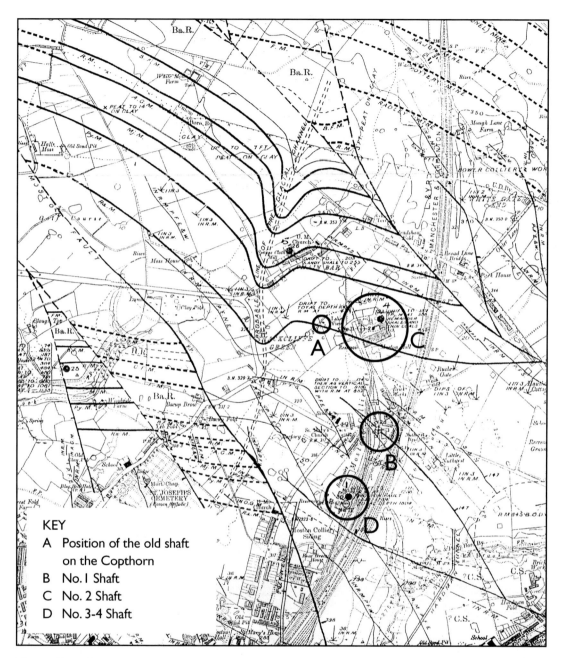

Figure 59: A Geological Survey Map of the area of the pit, dated 1923, showing Nos 1, 2, 3 and 4 shafts for Moston Colliery, but shows no marking for the Old shaft on the Copthorn. No 3, 4 shafts come in 1887 after the inundation in the old pit. Three boreholes have appeared on this map and numbered originally 4-5-25, but sometime later given the numbers 27-26 25 which appear on my next map. Extract courtesy of the British Geological Survey. 1923 Edition.

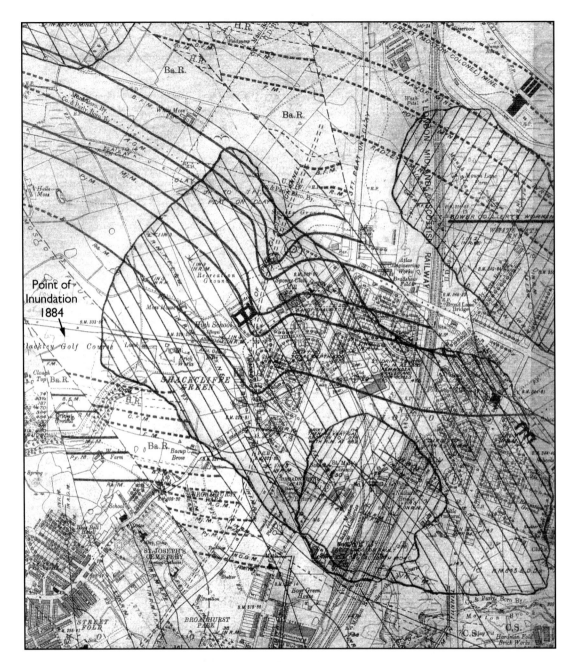

Figure 60: The Geological Survey people use short abbreviations to denote the names of the coal seams in the Manchester Coalfield when seen on their maps, ie Ra M = the Radley Mine Coal Seam, Py M = the Pottery Coal Seam and Mj M = the Major Mine Coal Seam. The line that this refers to is showing the exact places where the coal would outcrop and be seen, if no glacial debris stood above it.

The shaded areas with parallel lines denote the coal takes of various pits and in the larger area, Moston Colliery, this also denotes where flooding took place in the earlier pits No 1–2. The circular area that is shaded top right to bottom left, shows the position of the shaft pillar for the now flooded No 1 shaft, and as stated in the text was the only place where No 3–4 shafts could be sunk safely through those older flooded workings. The intact coal stopping the waters from getting down into the new pits Nos 3–4. Extract courtesy of the British Geological Survey. 1923 Edition.

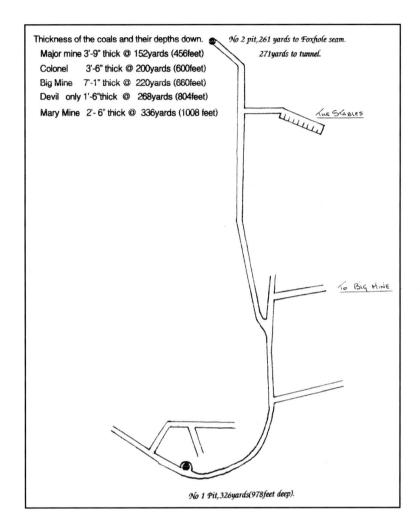

Figure 61: A Plan of the roadway in the Old Pit between No. 1 and No. 2 shafts, 1,000 feet below the surface, found among the abandonment plans still kept safe at Mansfield. Details of the coals known to have been available are also shown. Drawn from memory by H L Holliday.

Thickness of the coals and their depths down No. 2 pit:
261 yards to Foxhole seam.
Major mine 3ft 9ins thick @ 152 yards (456ft)
271 yards to tunnel.
Colonel 3ft 6ins thick @ 200 yards (600ft)
Big Mine 7ft1in thick @ 220 yards (660ft)
Devil only 1ft 6ins thick @ 268 yards (804ft)
Mary Mine 2ft 6ins thick @ 336 yards (1,008ft)
After the completion of my book, I visited the Coal Authority

The site that was Rerranti's at Moston, shortly after demolition work. Two of the pit boilers worked for many years supplying steam and heat for its Electrical workers in the factory.

The area of grass in the foreground is the place where No's 3–4 shafts stood. Bradford Court is in the background.

Looking towards the site of No 3–4 pits from 'The Fairway' road, 2004. Bradford Court the high flats, are the nearest buildings to the site of No 3 shaft of the late Moston Colliery. Its shaft was but yards away under the grass of a lawn area.

Addendum

Headquarters, based in Mansfield, Notts, to look at the abandonment plans for the Moston Collieries. These plans numbered close to 30; I have forgotten the exact number for it was a big job seeing them all in just one afternoon. There was one plan for each coal seam mined, from each shaft bottom, covering all the years of its working life as a coal pit. Finding that these plans were still in existence gave me great pleasure, and proved to me that what I have recorded in my book is true and accurate. Though all the plans were of interest in their own way, one stood out from the others if only for its great size, being so long that when placed upon a large map table, less than half was viewable at one time. This plan showed the Roger coal workings (the Miners called it Big Seam) stretching out from No. 3 shaft to a point far beyond the Roxy Cinema on Oldham Road, this road being drawn in on the map as a line of reference through Failsworth and Hollinwood.

Incidentally a part of Bower Collieries coal take was given to Moston Pit, after the Bower Colliery closed in 1923. The area covered by this map was marked off into small rectangles and a date was written into each one stating the year that the coal was actually taken from that one spot. These rectangles were all gently coloured in, so as to contrast one from another and so was recorded the 63 years of coal cutting and endeavour in one coal seam mined from No. 3 shaft. Each coal mined from No1-2-3 shafts, were shown on separate maps, each shaft of course being from different dates, but the same coal seams by name recurred in various places. My greatest disappointment, however, was that only four shafts were included in the records; the very first shaft, the Old Shaft on the Copthorn was not recorded. This was sunk by Mr John Stanley and vouched for as the sinker of the first successful shaft at Moston by no less than Joseph Dickinson, the first Inspector of Mines for Lancashire. I can only explain this by saying that his shaft was sunk in a time when secrecy was of the essence to a mine owner, and by the time the law was changed to make all pits produce plans of all of their worked ground, this old shaft had been replaced by two others (i.e. Nos 1 and 2), but both shafts still worked the same area of ground and mined the exact same coals as before. Indeed No. 2 shaft was less than 150 yards away from the position of Mr Stanley's first shaft. By the 1850s, Parliament was seeking ways of improving the coal industry's atrocious safety record and its poor working conditions for the men. The 1850 Act for the inspection of coal mines in Great Britain was a step in the right direction. It laid down four major improvements, one of which stated that plans of the mines must be kept at each pit, and produced for inspection when requested. John Stanley's Old Shaft on the Copthorn was before the date of the Act, hence no record of his shaft or his very earliest workings.

During my visit to the Coal Authority I learned that the waters that had to be pumped out of this wet colliery were piped up No. 3 shaft as far as the chamber at 623 feet below the surface, and then sent through a crosscut to finish their climb up No. 4 shaft and so into the reservoir behind the boiler house near the fence between the pit and Ferranti's works (see Figure 19). 144,000 gallons per week were being pumped up No. 4 shaft, this being the total from No. 3 and No. 4 shafts combined; No. 4 supplying 50,000 gallons from the older parts of the pit and No. 3 supplying 95,040 gallons.

In my story of the later pits (Nos 3 and 4) I state that no mining of coal took place below the area of the older flooded pit workings, but this is not quite true. A few years after the new pit opened in 1887, two of the early coals worked from No. 3 shaft were called the Platt Seam and the Black Mine Seam. No miner that I ever met spoke of these two coals; it was as if they had never existed, yet my own father took photos in or near both these places. An abandonment plan exists for both of these coals so now it all becomes clear to me where they were and why in my lifetime no one spoke or knew of these two coals at Moston. The area worked was below Broadhurst Park, the top end beneath the place that is now the bowling green and tennis courts, and lies 800 feet below those old flooded workings. In the east-west passage below No. 3 shaft, all the coals came from the east in the later days. The other direction led to the great wooden door that Thomas had never been through, so this was the way, after a turn to the north, where those mysterious coal seams had lain. The thick wooden door was closed for the last time in about 1933 and so Thomas Allen the pit Deputy for the Foxhole sector at Moston never knew what lay beyond those doors. Perhaps a realisation of the dangers closed the two coal seams down early, preventing any chance of a second drowned colliery below Moston. Those doors were closed before Thomas started work at the pit. The lack of a plan in the Coal Authority Archives showing details of the very first shaft, the Old Shaft on the Copthorn, though something of a disappointment to me, is nevertheless quite understandable at that early date being soon after 1820. However, proof that this shaft did exist is still to be found on old maps still in existence today. My heartfelt thanks go to the staff at the Mines Records Office at Bury Hill, 200 Lichfield Lane, Mansfield, Notts, for showing me these archives.

BIBLIOGRAPHY

Bairsto, H. 1991. *Just Henry*. Neil Richardson, 39 pp.

Becket, J. 1961. *Oldham Saturday Evening Chronical*, 18 March, 1961.

Dickinson, J. 1858. *Accident Report for 1858*. H. M. Inspector of Mines, pp. 36-40.

Dickinson, J. 1884. Discussion. *Transactions of the Manchester Geological Society*, **18**, p. 81.

Dickinson, J. 1898. Subsidence caused by colliery workings.*Transactions of the Manchester Geological Society*, **25**, pp. 583-612.

Dickinson, J. 1903. Discussion. *Transactions of the Manchester Geological Society*, **28**, pp. 147-161.

Evans, W. 1877. A description of the sinking through the quicksand and other deposits overlying the metals at Royton, Lancashire. *Transactions of the Manchester Geological Society*, **14**, pp. 178-186.

Harrison, G. B. 1911. Accidents in mines caused by falls of ground. (Presidental Address to the Manchester Geological and Mining Society.) *Transactions of the Manchester Geological and Mining Society*, **32**, pp.186-199.

Hayes, G. 2004. *Collieries and their Railways in the Manchester Coalfields,* 208pp. 2nd edition. Landmark Publishing. (revised and with additional text on the colliery railways, photos etc).

Hickling, G. 1927. *Sections of the strata of the Coal Measures of Lancashire*. The Lancashire and Chesire Coal Association.

Howarth, K. 1978. *Dark Day's*. The Greater Manchester Council. 127 pp. [Reprinted 1985.]

Hull, E. 1862. Marine fossils at Dukinfield. *Transactions of the Manchester Geological Society*, **3**, pp. 348-349.

March, M.C. 1918. The Superficial Geology of Manchester. *The Manchester Literary and Philosophical Society*, No. **11**, pp. 1-17.

National Coal Board, 1956. *Outlook,* **3**, No 7 [contained an Obituary with a photograph of my father].

Rance, C.E.de, 1884. The occurrence of brine in the Coal Measures. *Transactions of the Manchester Geological Society*, **18**, pp. 61-81.

Seale, Fr B. 1984. *The Moston Story*. 115 pp.

Simonin, L, 1869. *La Vie Souterrain: les mines et les mineurs*. Chapman & Hall, London. [English version.]

Tonks, L.H. *et al*. 1931. *Geology of Manchester and the South East Lancashire Coalfield*. H.M.S.O. 240 pp. [Reprinted 1970.]

Wild, G. 1881. On marine fossil shells at Ashton Moss Colliery sinking, nr Ashton under Lyne. *Transactions of the Manchester Geological Society*, **16**, pp.37-42.

INDEX

A

Aegiranum, marine fossil shells 77, 78, 79, 82
Allen, Thomas, [pit deputy] 4, 5, 54, 61, 93,
    94, 95, 101, 108, 110, 111, 112, 113, 121
anemometers 26
Ardwick Limestone mine 44

B

bell pit 11, 12
Big Mine 92, 109, 119
Black Mine 111, 120
Broughton Copper Company 29
Burnley 14

C

Carbonicola, fresh water fossil shells 80, 81,
    82, 85
Collieries
    Ashton Moss Colliery 78, 79, 100, 101,
        102, 122
    Bardsley Colliery 89
    Bradford Colliery 14, 72, 79, 81, 82, 98,
        99, 100, 102, 103, 107
    Moston Colliery 1, 2, 3, 5, 13, 14, 19,
        20, 21, 25, 27, 28, 29, 30, 34, 35, 36,
        37, 39, 42, 46, 52, 57, 58, 64, 65, 68,
        72, 79, 80, 81, 86, 87, 90, 91, 97, 100,
        102, 103, 104, 105, 106, 107, 108, 109,
        113, 117
    Oak Colliery 102, 114
    Woodpark Colliery 102
Colonel Mine 108
Copthorn Hill 32
corves 13, 20, 21, 26, 87
Crompton 16
Crompton Fold 16
Crompton Park 16

D

Davy Lamp 89
Dickinson, Joseph, H.M. inspector of Mines for
    Lancashire 35, 90, 97, 120
Doctor Clanny's Lamp 89
Dukinfield 14, 34, 78, 79, 89, 122
Dukinfield Marine Band, *[Aegiranum]* 77, 78,
    82

F

Failsworth, Locomotive 105
faulting 54, 58, 100
Foxholes 1 109

G

Great Nuthurst Hall 9, 16, 18

H

Hickling, Professor George 77
Holliday, Thomas 4, 5, 68, 113, 114
Hull, Edward of the Geological Survey 77

I

inclination 14, 79

L

Little Copthorn Hill 19, 21, 25
Little Nuthurst Hall 9
Longwall working 50

LANDMARK COLLECTOR'S LIBRARY

Images of Yorkshire Coal
Peter Williams
ISBN: 1 84306 151 1
192pp, 246 x 174mm, hardback, £19.99
Based upon the photographic collection held at
English Heritage National Monuments Record,
Swindon. Includes nearly 300 photographs of many
pits, a lot in their final years.

**Thunder Underground – Northumberland
Mining Disasters 1815-1865**
Roy Thompson
ISBN: 1 84306 169 4
192pp, 246 x 174mm, hardback, £19.95
The story of nine mining disasters on which inquests
were held before the controversial Stephen Reed,
Coroner for South Northumberland. With biographies
of the mine owners, The Viewers, Reed and a
description of the pits, the way they were worked and
of course details of the disasters.

Collieries in the North Staffordshire Coalfield
Paul Deakin
ISBN: 1 84306 138 4
160pp, 288 illustrations, 246 x 174mm,
hardback, £19.95
This book records the passing of one of the two most
dominant industries of The Potteries. It included many
scenes underground and nearly a third of the images
are in colour. Most scenes taken post-1947, but some
earlier ones included. Covers 30 pits.

Collieries of Somerset and Bristol
John Cornwell
ISBN: 1 84306 170 8
112pp, 246 x 174mm, paperback, £10.99
With over 85 rare photographs and text, this book
recalls the final days of the coalfield, including scenes
underground at three collieries – Kilmersdon,
Writhlington and Harry Stoke. It also includes photos
of the Kilmersdon Incline railway.

**Collieries and Their Railways in
the Manchester Coalfields**
Geoffrey Hayes
ISBN: 1 84306 135 X
208pp, 246 x 174mm, £19.95
121 illustrations (roughly 50% collieries, 50% railway
and locos) hardback

Pembrokeshire: The Forgotton Coalfield
M R Connop Price
ISBN: 1 84306 127 9
256pp; 246 x 174mm; many illustrations;
paperback, £17.95
A comprehensive study of the coalfield from the 13th
century to its closure in 1951. Includes transportation,
by land and sea and social history of the workforce.

**Ecton Copper Mines under the Dukes
of Devonshire 1760-90**
Lindsey Porter
ISBN: 1 84306 125 2
240pp, 246 x 174mm, many illustrations,
£19.95
Includes large section on Kingsley, Foxt and other
collieries in the Cheadle Coalfield. Ecton was possibly
the most profitable and deepest mine in the country
in the 1780s. Covers working of the mine, social
history, transportation, smelting.

The Mines of Devon
A K Hamilton Jenkin
ISBN: 1 84306 174 0
192pp, 246 x 174mm, paperback, £19.99
The only history to date on the extensive metalifferous
mining industry of Devon. Much of the text has only
been privately published previously. With a new
Introduction by Peter Claughton.

Landmark Publishing Ltd
Ashbourne Hall, Cokayne Ave
Ashbourne, Derbyshire DE6 1EJ England
Tel: (01335) 347349 Fax: (01335) 347303
e-mail: landmark@clara.net web site: www.landmarkpublishing.co.uk

Published by

Landmark Publishing Ltd
Ashbourne Hall, Cokayne Ave, Ashbourne, Derbyshire DE6 1EJ England
Tel: (01335) 347349 Fax: (01335) 347303
e-mail: landmark@clara.net
website: www.landmarkpublishing.co.uk

ISBN 1 84306 184 8

© **H. L. Holliday 2005**

Print: Bath Press Ltd, Bath

Design: Mark Titterton

Cover: James Allsopp

Front cover: A cross-measure roadway from Platt to Black Mine running through strong solid
ground supported by steel arching 6 feet by 6 feet. (Photo T Holliday 1929).

Page 3 & back cover top: Moston Best Coal" won first prize at the Newton Heath Parade of
1928. Those huge lumps were blocks of Roger Seam Coal. (Photo T. Holliday, taken across
Nuthurst Road towards the weighbridge; the pit stands behind it).

Back cover bottom: No. 1 pit, near to Nuthurst Bridge
(Photo reproduced with kind permission of Fr Brian Seale).